Printed at the Mathematical Centre, 49, 2e Boerhaavestraat, Amsterdam.

The Mathematical Centre, founded the 11-th of February 1946, is a non-profit institution aiming at the promotion of pure mathematics and its applications. It is sponsored by the Netherlands Government through the Netherlands Organization for the Advancement of Pure Research (Z.W.O), by the Municipality of Amsterdam, by the University of Amsterdam, by the Free University at Amsterdam, and by industries.

SUPEREXTENSIONS OF TOPOLOGICAL SPACES

BY A. VERBEEK

MATHEMATICAL CENTRE TRACTS 41

MATHEMATISCH CENTRUM AMSTERDAM 1972

CONTENTS

PREFACE

In this treatise we aim at giving a detailed introduction to the theory of superextensions of topological T_1-spaces. From an elementary point of view topological properties common to all superextensions are studied as well as e.g. properties that a superextension of a space X inherits from X.

The superextension λX of a T_1-space X is introduced by de Groot in [6], 1967. Every superextension λX is a (super-) compact T_1-space, in which X is embedded, and, as we shall prove in this treatise, it often has nice topological properties (local connectedness, connectedness, contractibility, compactness, extension of functions defined on X) and often it is quite large (strongly ∞-dimensional, and X is not dense in λX). In certain respects it resembles the hyperspace H(X) of all closed subsets of X (studied a.o. by Hausdorff, Vietoris, Michael and West). E.g. both extensions are conjectured to be homeomorphic to the Hilbert-cube if X is a metrizable, compact, absolute retract. (That $H([0,1]) = [0,1]^\infty$ was proved in 1971 by West and Schori, after having been an open problem for about 40 years.) But a non-degenerate Hausdorff space X is always closed (embedded) in H(X) and not in the compact space λX.

The construction of X however, bears close resemblance to another type of extension, viz. the Wallman-(type-)compactification $\omega(X)$, of X. Of course X is densely embedded in $\omega(X)$, but in general not in λX. If in the construction of $\omega(X)$ and in a convenient definition of compactness "finite" is suitably replaced by "two" then we obtain the superextension λX and a definition of supercompactness. Let us be a little more precise and first briefly review the Wallman-type-compactification.

All spaces under consideration are T_1-spaces. Let X be a T_1-space and $\mathcal{S}$ a subbase for the closed sets of X. The lemma of Alexander states that X is compact if and only if every (or equivalently: every maximal) centered subsystem of $\mathcal{S}$ (i.e. system with the finite intersection property) has a non-empty intersection.

Using this result one can compactify a non-compact space X, by adding all free maximal centered subsystems of $\mathcal{S}$ to X, and taking as a subbase for the closed sets of the so obtained set, all sets S^* for $S \in \mathcal{S}$, where $S^* = S \cup \{$all free maximal centered system containing S$\}$. It is easily verified that every centered subsystem of $\{S^* \mid S \in \mathcal{S}\}$ has a non-empty intersection, and according to the lemma of Alexander the extended space is compact. Indeed this is the Wallman-type-$\mathcal{S}$-compactification $\omega_{\mathcal{S}}X$, of X. (At this point we generalize slightly from the common definition of Wallman-type-compactification, that only consider closed bases S that are closed under the taking of finite unions and finite intersections.)

Instead of maximal centered systems of S we now consider subsystems of S that are maximal with respect to the property that every two members meet, and we thus obtain analogously the so-called *superextension of* X *relative* S, denoted by $\lambda_S X$. the mentioned subsystems of S are called *maximal linked systems* or *mls's*. The topology is defined just as above. Now the subbase for the closed sets $\{S^+ \mid S \in S\}$ satisfies the condition that every subsystem has a non-empty intersection not only if every finite number of elements has a non-empty intersection but already if (and only if) every two members meet. A space which has a closed subbase with this property is called *supercompact*. In terms of open sets it reads:

A topological space X is supercompact if X has an open subbase such that every cover of X by subbase elements has a subcover consisting of two elements.

Thus a superextension of X is a natural supercompact extension of X, in the same sense as a Wallman-type-compactification is a natural compact extension. Obviously each supercompact space is compact, while O'Connor has proved in [7] that at least every metrizable compact space also is supercompact.

The typical difference between λX and ωX lays in the socalled fmls's (mls's determined by finite sets). Throughout this treatise they are of invaluable help.

Now the main properties of superextensions are surveyed. For the sake of simplicity only *the* superextension of X is considered, i.e. the superextension λX relative the family of all closed sets.

Properties which λX possesses if and only if X does, are e.g. normality, separability or more generally the minimum cardinality of dense subsets (if X is infinite), its weight (if X is infinite, compact and Hausdorff), finiteness, strong 0-dimensionality, connectedness (cf. below), contractibility (if X is compact) and compact metrizability.

Especially with respect to connectedness and related properties λX behaves surprisingly nice: if X is connected then λX is not only connected but also locally connected. Moreover we can show that λX is contractible in each of the following cases: X is a finite polyhedron, X is the suspension of a compact T_1-space, or X is itself contractible and compact.

The closure of X in λX is homeomorphic to the Wallman-compactification

ωX. So in particular, if X is normal then

$$X \subset X^{-} \cong \beta X \cong \omega X \subset \lambda X$$

where βX is the Čech-Stone-compactification.

The superextension of a metrizable space M is metrizable if and only if M is compact (as can easily be seen from $\beta X \subset \lambda X$ for normal X and weight λX = weight X for compact Hausdorff X). So let us assume (M,d) is a compact metric space. We will show that d can easily be extended to a metric on all of λM. The dimension of λM is either zero (iff M is 0-dimensional) or stronly infinite.

If (N,d) is a non-compact metric space, then the superextension λN contains a dense, metrizable, nowhere locally compact subspace, which has the same weight as N. This subset again has nice properties; e.g. it is both connected and locally connected if X is connected, etc.

Miss G.A. Jensen proved, among some of the above results that a continuous function $f: X \rightarrow Y$ can be extended continuously to $\bar{f}: \lambda X \rightarrow \lambda Y$ if Y is normal. She also showed the existence of extensions to superextensions of X and Y relative certain subbases. This theorem yields e.g. that superextensions $\lambda_{\mathcal{S}}X$ of X relative a subbase $\mathcal{S}$ from a certain class (the normal subbases) are Hausdorff quotients of the superextension λX (relative all closed sets). So we can derive many properties of $\lambda_{\mathcal{S}}X$ for these $\mathcal{S}$, from our knowledge of λX.

For a better intuitive notion about superextensions it may be helpful to read chapter V, section 1, first. Here some superextensions of 'simple' spaces are described, such as the integers $\mathbb{Z}$, the reals $\mathbb{R}$, a circle, a converging pointsequence with its limit, and the Cantor discontinuum C ($\lambda C \cong C$).

The definition of supercompactness and superextension resulted from an investigation by de Groot and Aarts, [7] announced in 1966, in a topological characterization of complete regularity, in terms of the existence of a subbase for the topology endowed with certain geometric properties. Without defining superextensions they showed about that if such a subbase exists, then the closure of (the embedding of) X in λX is compact Hausdorff. There after de Groot defined supercompactness and superextensions in [6], and started the investigations, which were carried forward in several directions, a.o. by Császar, Hamburger, Jensen, O'Connor and the author. Császar made a more general approach, exposed in his survey paper [3], published in 1971. Hamburger particularly concentrated on characterizations of complete regularity and generalized the de Groot-Aarts result and several other results, see [10], preprint 1971. O'Connor proved the deep theorem on superconnectedness mentioned above, in 1968, see [15]. The consequences of this result are still not properly investigated, see also V.3. Jensen and the author did joint research in 1968 under supervision of professor J. de Groot. Their results have been published in [9]. Jensen proved a.o. the useful theorem on the extension of continuous functions, and results on the weight, o-dimensionality and separation axioms, while the author contributed a.o. theorems on (local) connectedness, contractibility and metrization. These results from [9] and those of de Groot and Aarts from [7] form an essential part of this treatise.

It is a pleasure to thank Miss A. Fasen for her patient typing and retyping the manuscript and drawing the figures, and Messrs. D. Zwarst, J. Suiker, J. Schipper, T. Baanders and J. Hillebrand for the printing.

CHAPTER I LINKED FAMILIES OF SETS

To get land's fruit in quantity
Takes jolts of labor ever more
Hence food will grow like one, two, three
While numbers grow like one, two, four.

(Song of Malthus)

A family of sets is said to be linked or a linked system if every two of its members meet. The set-theoretical superextension of a family of sets is the class of all "maximal linked subfamilies - mls's -" i.e. linked subfamilies that are not properly contained in any other linked subfamily. In this purely set-theoretical chapter we will study some combinatorial properties of (maximal) linked families and superextensions.

The first section contains the basic definitions, some examples and immediate consequences and a store of counterexamples for the other sections.

In section two the "finitely generated maximal linked systems - fmls's -" are introduced. These are the mls's that are "determined" by a finite family of finite sets. For an mls to be "determined by a family" means to be the only mls containing that family. This class of fmls's will be a useful tool in studying (topologized) superextensions, especially in III.3 and III.4 where separability, connectedness and local connectedness are concerned.

In section three we define an equivalence relation (on the class of all fmls's only) roughly speaking as follows: If M and N are fmls's consisting of subsets of X and Y respectively, and there exists a bijection (function) $f: X \to Y$ such that $N = f(M) = \{f(S) \mid S \in M\} = \{\{f(x) \mid x \in S\} \mid S \in M\}$, then we say that type M = type N (type $M \geq$ type N respectively). In this section particular attention is also paid to the number of mls's in the powerset of an n-point-set. This interest is justified because each fmls is of the same type as some mls in the powerset of a finite set. Hence this provides a description of all fmls's. So far this number $\lambda(n)$ is only known for $n \leq 7$. A calculation of $\lambda(n)$ is presented for $n \leq 6$, plus the outline of an algorithm that was used by A.E. Brouwer to calculate $\lambda(7)$ on a computer. For $n = 0,1,2,3,4,5,6,7$ the number $\lambda(n)$ equals respectively 1, 1, 2, 4, 12, 81,

2646, 1422564, which seems predicted by the song of Malthus.

Related to fmls's are the mls's that consist of finite sets only; these are discussed in section four. Maybe surprisingly this class strictly contains the class of all fmls's. I.e. there exist mls's that consist of finite sets only but are not "determined" by any finite subfamily (of finite sets). Some problems and results in sections two, three and four seem to be interesting not only because of their consequences in topological superextensions but also from a purely combinatorial point of view.

Finally section five presents the concept of prime families, which is in some sense dual to the finite intersection property (cf. I.5.1.ii). In the next chapter this will lead to a useful relation between mls's and maximal centered systems (cf. II.5).

I.1. DEFINITIONS

I.1.1. NOTATION

$PX = P(X)$ is the powerset of X, for any set X.

$P_f X = P_f(X)$ is the set of all finite subsets of X.

$P_{cof} X = P_{cof}(X) = \{X' \subset X \mid X \backslash X' \text{ is finite}\}$.

$\mathbb{R}$ is the set of real numbers, possibly endowed with the Euclidean topology.

$\mathbb{Z}$ is the set of integers.

$\mathbb{N}$ is the set of positive integers.

$\mathbb{R}^n$ is the n-dimensional Euclidean topological space.

Next we define some fundamental intersection properties of families of sets. The words family and system are used as synonyms.

A family of sets is *fixed* if its intersection is non-empty.

A family of sets is *centered* or *has the f.i.p.* if each finite subfamily has a non-empty intersection.

A family of sets is *linked* if every two sets meet.

A family of sets is *free* if its intersection is empty.

A family of sets $\{S_\alpha \mid \alpha \in J\}$ is *quasi-disjoint* if every two sets have the same set for intersection. More precisely if for some fixed set K, the *kernel* of the family, and for each pair $\alpha, \alpha' \in J$ $\quad S_\alpha \cap S_{\alpha'} = K$ (if $\alpha \neq \alpha'$).

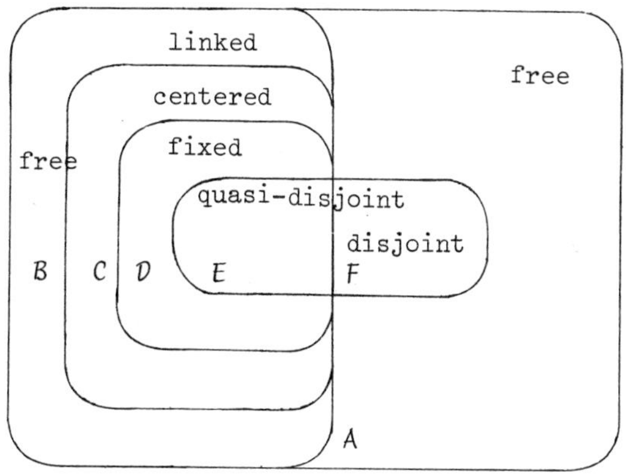

subfamilies of a family of sets, S

S	$= A \cup B \cup C \cup D \cup E \cup F$
free	$= A \cup B \cup C \cup F$
linked	$= B \cup C \cup D \cup E$
centered	$= C \cup D \cup E$
fixed	$= D \cup E$
quasi-disjoint	$= E \cup F$
disjoint	$= F$

I.1.2.

Let S be any family of sets. As a guide for the imagination the reader is informed that furtheron we restrict to the following:
in Chapter II, III: S is a family of closed subsets of a T_1-space which constitutes a subbase for all closed sets.
in Chapter IV: G is the family of all closed subsets of a topological space (T_1, metric, and compact metric resp.)

We say that a subfamily M of S is a *maximal linked system* or *mls (in S)* if M is linked but not properly contained in any other linked subfamily of S.

Note that if $M \subset S$ is linked, then also any subfamily of M is linked. Moreover, by Zorn's or Teichmüller-Tuckey's lemma M is contained in at least one subfamily of S that is maximally linked.

I.1.3. EXAMPLES

(a) Any fixed family and any centered family is linked.

(b) Let $\mathcal{S} = P\{1,2,3\}$. There is just one free mls in $\mathcal{S}$:

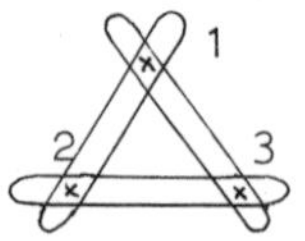

$$\{\{1,2\},\{2,3\},\{3,1\},\{1,2,3\}\}.$$

The reader is requested to notice explicitly that this linked family is indeed maximally linked.

(c) Let X be a set and $\mathcal{S}$ a family of subsets of X containing all singletons. Then an mls $\mathcal{M}$ in $\mathcal{S}$ is fixed iff it contains a singelton. If $\{x\} \in \mathcal{M}$ then

$$\mathcal{M} = \{S \mid x \in S \in \mathcal{S}\}.$$

(d) Let X be a set again and $\mathcal{S}$ a family of subsets of X containing all finite subsets (e.g. $\mathcal{S}$ is the family of all closed sets in a T_1-space X). Let $G \in \mathcal{S}$ and $p \in X$. First suppose G is not a singleton and $x \notin G$. Then the family $\mathcal{M}$ of all elements of $\mathcal{S}$ that either contain G or contain x and meet G is a free mls in $\mathcal{S}$. This mls $\mathcal{M}$ is uniquely "determined" by its elements G and all $\{p,x\}$, $x \in G$, in the sense that $\mathcal{M}$ is the only mls in $\mathcal{S}$ containing these sets.

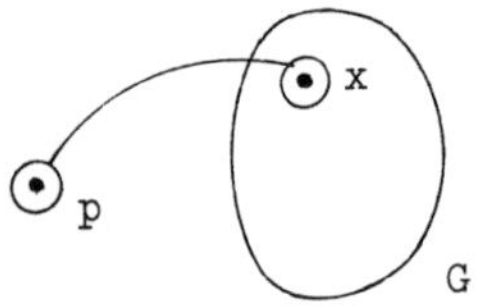

In the degenerate case that $G = \{q\}$ one sees that $\{q\} \in \mathcal{M}$ and consequently $\mathcal{M} = \{S \mid q \in S \in \mathcal{S}\}$ is fixed. In the other degenerate case, viz. $p \in G$, $\mathcal{M}$ is also fixed, but now $\mathcal{M} = \{S \mid p \in S \in \mathcal{S}\}$.

(e) If $\mathcal{M}$, $\mathcal{N}$ and $\mathcal{P}$ are three mls's in the powerset of some fixed set, then so is

$$(\mathcal{M} \cap \mathcal{N}) \cup (\mathcal{N} \cap \mathcal{P}) \cup (\mathcal{P} \cap \mathcal{M}).$$

If $\mathcal{M} = \mathcal{N}$, then the above mls also equals $\mathcal{M}$.

(f) Let $\mathcal{S}$ be closed under the taking of finite intersections. Then any maximal centered subfamily of $\mathcal{S}$ is also an mls.

I.1.4. PROPOSITION

Let $\mathcal{M}$ and $\mathcal{N}$ be mls's in some family $\mathcal{S}$.

(a) $\emptyset \notin \mathcal{M}$

(b) *If* $S \in \mathcal{M}$, $T \in \mathcal{S}$ *and* $S \subset T$ *then* $T \in \mathcal{M}$

(c) *If* $S \in \mathcal{S} \setminus \mathcal{M}$ *then* $\exists T \in \mathcal{M} \quad S \cap T = \emptyset$

(d) $\mathcal{M} \neq \mathcal{N}$ *iff* $\exists S \in \mathcal{M}, \exists T \in \mathcal{N} \quad S \cap T = \emptyset$

PROOF

(a), (b) and (c) are trivial, and also the if-part of (d). Assume $\mathcal{M} \neq \mathcal{N}$. Because of the maximality of $\mathcal{M}$: $\exists S \in \mathcal{M} \setminus \mathcal{N}$. Now by (c): $\exists T \in \mathcal{N} \quad S \cap T = \emptyset$.

I.1.5.

Let us modify example I.1.3.b a little. Suppose $\mathcal{S}$ is a family of subsets of an infinite set X containing all finite subsets of X, in formula:

$$P_f X \subset \mathcal{S} \subset PX.$$

For any three different points p, q, r the following family $\mathcal{M}_{pqr}$ is a free mls.

$$\mathcal{M}_{pqr} = \{S \in \mathcal{S} \mid S \text{ contains at least two points of } p, q \text{ and } r\}.$$

This mls has minimal sets: {p,q}, {q,r}, {r,p} which uniquely determine $\mathcal{M}_{pqr}$ in the sense that $\mathcal{M}_{pqr}$ is the only mls in $\mathcal{S}$ containing these three sets. This is formalized in the following definitions.

Let $\mathcal{S}$ be any family of sets. A subfamily $\mathcal{M} \subset \mathcal{S}$ is called a *pre-mls* if $\mathcal{M}$ is contained in precisely one mls in $\mathcal{S}$, i.e. if $\mathcal{M}$ is linked and contained in at most one mls. We say that this mls is *determined* by $\mathcal{M}$, and it will be denoted by $\underline{\mathcal{M}}$. We also say that $\mathcal{M}$ is a *pre-mls for* $\underline{\mathcal{M}}$.

Some pre-mls's are smaller and easier to describe than the mls's they determine. E.g. in the example given above {{p,q},{q,r},{r,p}} is a pre-mls for $\mathcal{M}_{pqr}$ and in example I.1.3.d the family $\{G,\{p,x\} \mid x \in G\}$ is a pre-mls for $\mathcal{M}$. This will be elaborated in the concept "finitely generated mls".

An mls $\mathcal{M}$ is said to be *defined on* some set M or M is *a defining set for* $\mathcal{M}$ if

$$\forall S \in \mathcal{M}\ \exists S' \in \mathcal{M} \quad S' \subset S \cap M.$$

If $\mathcal{M}$ is defined on M but not on any proper subset of M, then M is called *the* (*smallest*, cf. I.1.11.c) *defining set* for M.

An mls M is called *finitely generated* or an *fmls* if it has a finite defining set, and an n-mls if it has a smallest defining set of n points. In both cases we require that S contains all finite subsets of $\cup S$.

I.1.6.

The *set-theoretical superextension* of a family S, denoted by $\lambda(S)$ is defined as the class of all maximal linked subsystems of S. Notations:

$$\lambda(S) = \{M\subset S \mid M \text{ is an mls in } S\}$$

$$\lambda_f(S) = \{M\subset S \mid M \text{ is an fmls in } S\}$$

$$\lambda_n(S) = \{M\subset S \mid M \text{ is a k-mls for some } k\leq n\} \quad (n=1,2,3,\ldots).$$

I.1.7.

If M is any subfamily of S then an element $S \in M$ is called *minimal* in M if it is $\subset$-minimal, i.e. if no proper subset of S also belongs to M. Notation:

$$M_{MIN} = \{S\in M \mid \forall T\in M\ T\subset S \Rightarrow T=S\}.$$

Of course an mls need not contain any minimal sets, cf. I.1.3.f, and if it contains minimal sets, then these do not necessarily form a pre-mls. Finally if the minimal sets do constitute a pre-mls, then this needs not be a smallest pre-mls, as examples I.1.8.a and b will show. However, in two important cases, viz. for fmls's and in case S is the family of all closed sets in a compact space, each mls has a pre-mls, consisting just of the minimal sets. Moreover their union, clearly, is the smallest defining set of the mls. For fmls's this pre-mls also is the smallest pre-mls, but in the other case this need not be true, see I.1.8.b and I.1.10.d.

I.1.8. EXAMPLES

(a) Let S be the family of closed intervals of the unit circle in the plane

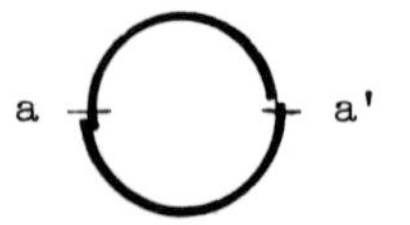

$\mathbb{R}^2$. The family M of all intervals of length $\geq \pi$ is a free mls in S. The minimal sets of M are all intervals of length π, and they constitute a pre-mls. If any interval I of length π is deleted from

M_{MIN}, then it is easily seen that any mls N containing all remaining intervals also must contain the deleted interval I and thus $N = M$. I.e. $M_{MIN}\backslash\{I\}$, $I \in M_{MIN}$ also is a pre-mls for M, and N has no smallest pre-mls.

For any autohomeomorphism ϕ of the circle, that is not a rotation, also $\{I \in S \mid \text{length } \phi^{-1} \geq \pi\}$ is an mls, which differs from M.

In the family G of all closed subsets of the circle, M is not an mls or pre-mls: for every pair of anti-podal points $\{a,a'\}$ one easily sees that $M \cup \{a,a'\}$ is linked. If we extend this family to an mls $M_{a,a'}$ in G, then $M_{a,a'} \neq M_{b,b'}$ if a,a' and b,b' are different pairs of antipodal points.

(b) Suppose G is the family of all closed subsets of the closed unit interval [0,1] and μ is the ordinary measure on [0,1]. Put

$$M = \{S \in G \mid \mu(S) \geq \tfrac{1}{2}\}.$$

Then M is an mls in G, and

$$M_{MIN} = \{S \in G \mid \mu(S) = \tfrac{1}{2}\}$$

is a pre-mls for M. Again we claim that for any $S \in M_{MIN}$ also $M_{MIN}\backslash\{S\}$ is a pre-mls for M. For this it suffices to show that if $T \in G$ meets all $S' \in M_{MIN}\backslash\{S\}$, then $T \cap S \neq \emptyset$. Suppose $T \in G$ and $T \cap S = \emptyset$. Then $X\backslash(T \cup S)$ is a non-empty, open subset of X, so $\mu(X\backslash(T \cup S)) > 0$. Choose two closed subsets F and G of X such that

$$\mu F = \mu G > 0$$

$$F \subset X\backslash(T \cup S)$$

$$G \subset S$$

Put $S' = (F \cup S\backslash G)^{-}$. Then $\mu(S') = \frac{1}{2}$, so $S' \in M_{MIN}\backslash\{S\}$. However $S' \cap T \subset (F \cap T) \cup (S \cap T) = \emptyset$, a contradiction. Again the conclusion must be that M contains no smallest pre-mls.

(c) There exist mls's of finite sets with infinitely many minimal sets. However, in accordance to I.5.2, there are only finitely many minimal sets of k points for each fixed finite number k. Hence there are only countable many minimal sets.

Let $S = P_f\{0,\pm 1,\pm 2,\pm 3,\ldots\}$ and define $M = \{M_k \mid k = \pm 1, \pm 2, \ldots\}$ as follows:

$M_k = \{-k, 0, 1, 2, \ldots, k-1\}$ for $k > 0$,

$M_k = \{k, k+1, \ldots, -2, -1, -k\}$ if $k < 0$.

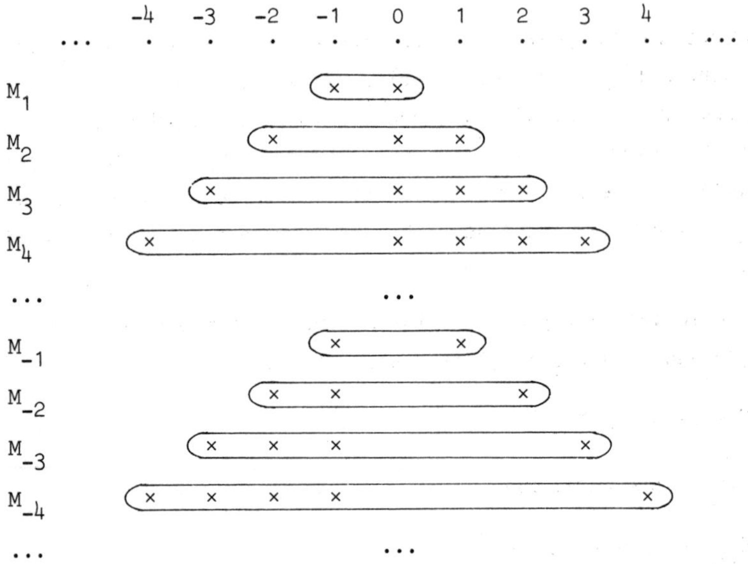

We make the following observations:

(i) M *is a pre-mls because* $M' = \{S' \in S \mid \exists S \in M \;\; S \subset S'\}$ *is an mls.*

PROOF

Clearly M' is linked, suppose M' is not maximally linked, i.e. $\exists T \in S \setminus M' \;\; M' \cup \{T\}$ is linked. Then choose $m \leq 0$ minimal and $n \geq -1$ maximal such that

$$\{m, m+1, \ldots, -1\} \subset T$$

and

$$\{0, 1, \ldots, n\} \subset T.$$

Because $T \notin M'$ we find that if $m \leq -1$ then $\{0,1,2,3,\ldots,|m|\} \cap T = \emptyset$, because if $i \in \{1,2,3,\ldots,|m|\} \cap T$, then $M_{-i} \subset T$ and if $0 \in T$ then $M_1 \in T$. However as consequence we obtain that

$$\{m-1, 0, 1, 2, \ldots, |m|\} = M_{|m|+1}$$

is disjoint of T, a contradiction.
If $n \geq 0$ then similarly $M_{-n-1} = \{-n-1,-n,\ldots,0,-2,-1,n+1\}$ does not meet T, also a contradiction. Finally if $n = -1$ and $m = 0$, then $\{0,-1\} \cap T = M_1 \cap T = \emptyset$.

(ii) No proper subsystem of $\mathcal{M}$ *is a pre-mls.*

PROOF

For any $k > 1$

$$(\mathcal{M}\backslash\{M_k\}) \cup \{\{-k,-k+1,\ldots,-1,0,1,\ldots,k+1\}\backslash M_k\}$$

also is linked.
For $k < 0$

$$(\mathcal{M}\backslash\{M_k\}) \cup \{\{ k-1,k,\ldots,-1,0,1,\ldots,k\}\backslash M_k\}$$

is linked.
And finally

$$(\mathcal{M}\backslash\{M_1\}) \cup \{\{-2,1\}\}$$

is linked.

(iii) Every M_k *is minimal in* $\mathcal{M}$*, and hence also in* $\mathcal{M}'$.

PROOF

For $0 < k < 1$

$$M_{-k} \cap M_1 = \{k\}$$

and

$$M_k \cap M_{-1} = \{-k\}.$$

This means that every point of M_k is "needed" to make $\mathcal{M}$ linked.

(iv) $\mathcal{M}$ *is not a pre-mls in* $P\{0,\pm1,\pm2,\ldots\}$.

PROOF

If $\mathcal{N},\mathcal{N}'$ are mls's in $P\{0,\pm1,\pm2,\ldots\}$ containing $\mathcal{M} \cup \{\{0,1,2,3,\ldots\}\}$ and $\mathcal{M} \cup \{\{-1,-2,-3,\ldots\}\}$ respectively then $\mathcal{N} \neq \mathcal{N}'$.

(v) The only two mls's in $P\{0,\pm1,\pm2,\ldots\}$ *that contain* M *have the following pre-mls's:*

$$N_1 = M \cup \{\{0,1,2,3,\ldots\}\}$$

and

$$N_2 = M \cup \{\{-1,-2,-3,\ldots\}\}.$$

PROOF

Suppose $S \subset \{0,\pm1,\pm2,\ldots\}$ and $M \cup \{S\}$ is linked, while S does not contain a set of M. Then, because $\{0,-1\} \in M$ either $0 \in S$ and $-1 \notin S$ or $-1 \in S$ and $0 \notin S$. First suppose $0 \in S$ and $-1 \notin S$. Because $\{\pm1\} \in M$, $S \cap \{\pm1\} \neq \emptyset$, i.e. $+1 \in S$. Because $\{-2,0,1\} \in M$, $\{-2,0,1\} \not\subset S$, hence $-2 \notin S$. Because $\{-2,-1,2\} \in M$, $\{-2,-1,2\} \cap S \neq \emptyset$, i.e. $2 \in S$. And so on. Thus we find that $S = \{0,1,2,\ldots\}$. Because of the symmetry (reflection at $-\frac{1}{2}$), if $-1 \in S$ and $0 \in S$ then $S = \{-1,-2,\ldots\}$. This shows that if $S \subset \{0,\pm1,\pm2,\ldots\}$ and $N_i \cup \{S\}$ is linked, then S must contain a member of N_i, $i = 1,2$. It easily follows that N_i is a pre-mls. On the other hand if N is an mls in $P\{0,\pm1,\pm2,\ldots\}$ containing M, then $\exists S \in N \neg \exists T \in M \quad T \subset S$. Clearly $N_i \subset N$ for some $i = 1,2$.

(d) (cf. [7], §3 example 2 p. 102-103)
If M is a pre-mls in S then the mls $\underline{M}$ that contains M of course contains $\{S' \in S \mid \exists S \in M \quad S \subset S'\}$, but $\underline{M}$ may be strictly larger, as we saw in (a) and (b) if we take there M = all minimal sets except one ($\underline{M}$ = all intervals of length $\geq \frac{1}{2}$ on the unit circle respectively $\underline{M}$ = all closed subsets of $[0,1]$ with measure $\geq \frac{1}{2}$). Now we will give an example, where even $\underline{M}$ is not defined on $\cup M$.
Let X be the union of the four disjoint infinite sets A, B, C and D.

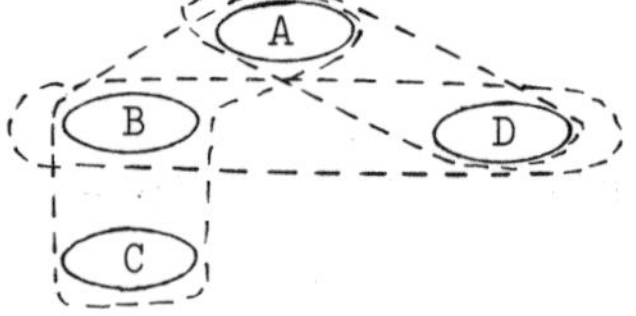

Recall that we denote the family of all cofinite subsets of a set Y (i.e. subsets of Y with a finite complement) by $P_{cof}(Y)$. S is defined as the family consisting of $A \cup B \cup C$, $D \cup A$ and all finite and cofinite subsets of X and of $B \cup D$. In formula:

$$S = P_f(X) \cup P_{cof}(X) \cup P_{cof}(B \cup D) \cup \{A \cup B \cup C,\ D \cup A\}.$$

The only free maximal centered systems in S are:

$$M_1 = P_{cof}(X) \cup \{A \cup B \cup C\} \cup P_{cof}(B \cup D),$$

$$M_2 = P_{cof}(X) \cup \{D \cup A\} \cup P_{cof}(B \cup D) \quad \text{and}$$

$$M_3 = P_{cof}(X) \cup \{D \cup A,\ A \cup B \cup C\}.$$

Note that $S \backslash P_f(X) = M_1 \cup M_2 = M_1 \cup M_2 \cup M_3$ is maximally linked. Thus $S \backslash P_f(X)$ is the only mls not containing any finite set. On the other hand any mls containing either M_1, M_2 or M_3 will also not contain any finite set. This implies that M_1, M_2 and M_3 are pre-mls for $S \backslash P_f(X)$. Now put

$$N = \{D \cup A\} \cup P_{cof}(B \cup D)$$

then N is a linked subfamily of S, and $N \cup \{F\}$, $F \in P_f X$, is not linked. Hence N is a pre-mls for $S \backslash P_f(X)$. However

$$M_2 = \{S' \in S' \mid \exists S \in N \quad S \subset S'\} \neq S \backslash P_f(X)$$

and

$$\cup N = A \cup B \cup D = X \backslash C,$$

whilst $S \backslash P_f(X)$ is defined only on the whole X, because $D \cup A \in (S \backslash P_f(X))_{MIN}$ and $A \cup B \cup C \in (S \backslash P_f(X))_{MIN}$.

The basic properties of pre-mls's, minimal sets etc. are contained in the following propositions:

I.1.9. PROPOSITION ON PRE-MLS'S

Let M be an mls in some family S.

(a) *A subfamily $P \subset S$ is a pre-mls iff*

$$\forall S,S' \in S \quad (P \cup \{S\} \text{ and } P \cup \{S'\} \text{ are linked} \Longrightarrow S \cap S' \neq \emptyset).$$

(b) *If $P \subset S$ is a pre-mls for M then*

$$M = \underline{P} = \{S \in S \mid P \cup \{S\} \text{ is linked}\}$$

(c) *If* $M' \subset M$ *satisfies* $\forall S \in M \, \exists S' \in M' \;\; S' \subset S$ *then* M' *is a pre-mls for* M *and* M *is defined on* $\cup M'$.

(d) *Suppose* $\mathcal{S}$ *is the family of closed subsets of a compact space* X *and* M *is an mls in* $\mathcal{S}$. *Then every element of* M *contains a minimal element of* M, *so* M_{MIN} *is a pre-mls for* M *and* $\cup M_{MIN}$ *is the smallest defining set of* M.
For $S \in M_{MIN}$ $\;M_{MIN}\backslash\{S\}$ *is a pre-mls for* M *iff each neighbourhood of* S *contains another* $S' \in M_{MIN}$. *So* M_{MIN} *need not be a minimal pre-mls.*

PROOF

(a) "If" part. Under the condition $\{S\in\mathcal{S} \mid P\cup\{S\}$ is linked$\}$ is linked, and clearly also maximally linked. On the other hand if M is an mls, containing P, then $M \subset \{S\in\mathcal{S} \mid P\cup\{S\}$ is linked$\}$. So this mls is the only one containing P.

"Only if" part. Suppose $\exists S, S' \in \mathcal{S} \;\; P \cup \{S\}$ and $P \cup \{S'\}$ are linked and $S \cap S' = \emptyset$. Choose mls's M and M' containing $P \cup \{S\}$ and $P \cup \{S'\}$ respectively. Clearly $M \neq M'$.

(b) follows directly from the proof of (a), while

(c) is trivial.

(d) Let $S \in M$. Choose a maximal (in M) centered subfamily M' of M containing S. Put $S' = \cap M'$. If $S^* \in M$ then $M' \cup \{S^*\}$ is linked, and because intersections of finitely many elements of M' again belong to M', $M' \cup \{S^*\}$ has the f.i.p. Because X is compact we have $S' \cap S^* = \cap(M'\cup\{S^*\}) \neq \emptyset$. Hence $S' \in M$ and $S' \subset S$.

By (c) M_{MIN} is a pre-mls for M and $\cup M_{MIN}$ is a defining set for M. If $M' \subsetneq \cup M_{MIN}$, then we may choose an $S \in M_{MIN}$ with $S\backslash M' \neq \emptyset$. Because no subset of S belongs to M, this shows that M' cannot be a defining set for M.

If $S \in M_{MIN}$ and $M_{MIN}\backslash\{S\}$ is a pre-mls for M and $S \subset U$, U open in X, then $(M_{MIN}\backslash\{S\}) \cup \{X\backslash U\}$ cannot be linked, because $X\backslash U \in \mathcal{S}\backslash M$. Hence $\exists S' \in M_{MIN} \;\; S' \neq S$ and $S' \cap X\backslash U = \emptyset$, i.e. $S' \subset U$.

If $S \in M_{MIN}$, each neighbourhood of S contains another $S' \in M_{MIN}$ and F is an arbitrary closed subset of X, but $F \cap S = \emptyset$, then clearly $M_{MIN} \cup \{F\}\backslash\{S\}$ is not linked. I.e. any mls containing $M_{MIN}\backslash\{S\}$ contains S, thus contains M_{MIN}, and so must be equal to M.

I.1.10. PROPOSITION ON MINIMAL SETS

(a) *If* $S \in M \in \lambda(\mathcal{S})$, S *is finite and* $P(S) \subset \mathcal{S}$, *then* S *is minimal iff*

$$\forall p \in S \exists T \in M \quad T \cap S = \{p\}.$$

(b) *If* $\mathcal{S}$ *is the family of closed subsets of a topological* T_1*-space and* $S \in M \in \lambda(\mathcal{S})$, *then* $S \in M_{MIN}$ *iff for every open* O *in* X *either* $O \cap S = \emptyset$ *or*

$$\exists S' \in M \quad S \cap S' \subset O.$$

The trivial proof is omitted.

I.1.11. PROPOSITION ON DEFINING SETS

Suppose $M \in \lambda(\mathcal{S})$ *for some family* $\mathcal{S}$.

(a) $\cup\mathcal{S}$ *is a defining set for* M.

(b) *If* $S,T \in \mathcal{S}$ *and* $S \cup T$ *is a defining set for* M, *then* $S \in M$ *or* $T \in M$.

(c) *If* M *and* M' *are defining sets for* M, *then so is* $M \cap M'$. *So if* M *has a minimal defining set, then it is the (unique) smallest defining set of* M.

REMARK

Note that (b) cannot be generalized to arbitrary finite unions as I.1.3.b shows: $\{\{1,2\},\{2,3\},\{3,1\},\{1,2,3\}\}$ is defined on $\{1\} \cup \{2\} \cup \{3\}$.

PROOF

(a) is trivial.

(b) Suppose $S,T \notin M$. Then $\exists S',T' \in M \quad S \cap S' = T \cap T' = \emptyset$. But the definition of defining set $\exists S'',T'' \in M \quad S'' \subset S' \cap (S\cup T)$ and $T'' \subset T' \cap (S\cup T)$. Now $S'' \cap T'' = \emptyset$, for $S'' \cap T'' \subset S' \cap T' \cap (S\cup T) = \emptyset$, a contradiction.

(c) If $S \in M$ then, because M is defined on M, $\exists S' \in M \quad S' \subset S \cap M$, and because M is defined on M', $\exists S'' \in M \quad S'' \subset S' \cap M' \subset S \cap (M\cap M')$.

I.1.12. PROPOSITION

For any family S containing all finite subsets of $\cup S$:

$$\lambda_1(S) = \lambda_2(S) \subset \lambda_3(S) \subset \lambda_4(S) \subset \ldots \bigcup_{n\in\mathbb{N}} \lambda_n(S) = \lambda_f(S) \subset \lambda(S).$$

REMARK

The condition on S is needed because otherwise $\lambda_n(S)$ and $\lambda_f(S)$ are not defined (see I.1.5). The only thing to prove is $\lambda_1(S) = \lambda_2(S)$ which is left as an exercise for the reader.

I.2. FINITELY GENERATED MAXIMAL LINKED SYSTEMS

I.2.1.

THROUGHOUT THIS SECTION S *IS A FAMILY WHICH CONSISTS OF SUBSETS OF SOME SET* X, *AND CONTAINS ALL FINITE SUBSETS OF* X:

$$P_f(X) \subset S \subset P(X).$$

The (free) maximal centered subsystems of S and the (free) mls's in S show the remarkable difference that the former will never contain finite or minimal sets. This makes maximal centered systems, and those mls's that do not contain a pre-mls of minimal sets hard to describe in a constructive sense. However those mls's whose minimal sets constitute a pre-mls, i.e. determine the whole mls, are much easier to handle. Especially, of course, if moreover the number of minimal sets is finite. The mls's for which this holds are precisely the fmls's (cf. I.2.3). The role fmls's play in super-extensions, explains in part the combinatorial nature of so many proofs.

If we topologize the family of maximal centered systems in S in the well-known way, thus obtaining the Wallman-type S-compactification of X, then X is (canonically) densely embedded. However, once we have introduced a corresponding topology on $\lambda(S)$, wherein X is also canonically embedded, then we will see that X is not dense in $\lambda(S)$ - at least not if X is Hausdorff and has at least 3 points (cf. II.1.8) -. Indeed each free finitely generated mls does not belong to the closure of X if X is Hausdorff. On the other hand, the family of all finitely generated mls's, denoted by $\lambda_f(S)$, will be dense in $\lambda(S)$. This will be a powerful tool in studying connectedness and separability of $\lambda(S)$ (cf. II.8 and II.9).

I.2.2.

First we will observe that finite linked families which are pre-mls's "behave nice":

PROPOSITION

If a finite family of sets $A = \{A_0,\dots,A_n\}$, *none of which contains another, is a pre-mls in* S, *then*

(i) $\forall A \in A \quad \forall a \in A \; \exists A' \in A \qquad A \cap A' = \{a\}$

and so each $A \in A$ *is finite.*

Moreover for a finite family $A = \{A_0,\dots,A_n\}$, *of finite sets, the following conditions are equivalent:*

(ii) A *is a pre-mls in* S

(iii) $\{S \in S \mid \exists A \in A \quad A \subset S\}$ *is an mls in* S

(iv) $\forall T \subset \cup A \quad \exists A \in A \quad A \subset T$ or $A \subset (\cup A) \setminus T$

(v) A *is a pre-mls in* $P(\cup A)$.

COROLLARY

If M *is a finite subset of* $X = \cup S$, *and* M *is an mls in* $P(M)$, *then* M *is a pre-mls in* S, *and* $\underline{M} = \{S \in S \mid \exists A \in M \quad A \subset S\}$ *is an fmls.*

REMARK

If a finite family A of (necessarily finite) sets satisfies (i) then it need not be a pre-mls. Put $X = \{1,2,3,4,5\}$ and $A = \{\{1,2,3\},\{1,4,5\},\{2,4,5\},\{3,4,5\},\{2,3,4\},\{2,3,5\}\}$. Then both $\{1,2,4\}$ and $\{3,5\}$ meet all sets of A, so A is not a pre-mls.

PROOF

(i) Suppose, on the other hand that for $A \in A$, say for A_0, and some $a \in A_0$, we have $A_0 \cap A_i \neq \{a\}$, for $i = 1,\dots,n$. Then $A_i \cap A_0 \setminus \{a\} \neq \emptyset$, for $i = 1,\dots,n$. As no set in A contains another we may choose $a_i \in A_i \setminus A_0$. Now the disjoint sets $A_0 \setminus \{a\}$ and $\{a_0,a_1,\dots,a_n\}$ both meet all sets of A, so A is not a pre-mls (by I.1.9.a).

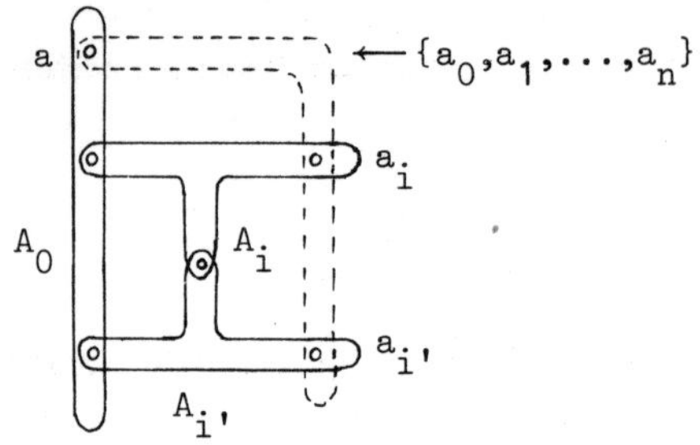

(ii) $\Longrightarrow$ (v) is trivial.

(v) $\Longrightarrow$ (iv) Let M be the mls in $P(\cup A)$ containing A. By I.1.11.b either $T \in M$ or $(\cup A \setminus T) \notin M$; let us suppose $T \in M$. So $(\cup A \setminus T) \in M$. Then $\exists A \in A$ such that $A \cap (\cup A \setminus T) = \emptyset$, i.e. $A \subset T$.

(iv) $\Longrightarrow$ (iii) Suppose $S \in S$ and $A \cup \{S\}$ is linked. Then by (iv) $\exists A \in A \quad A \subset (S \cap \cup A) \subset S$ or $A \subset (\cup A) \setminus S$, and the last possibility obviously is excluded, i.e. $\exists A \in A \quad A \subset S$. Thus $\underline{A} = \{S \in S \mid \exists A \in A \quad A \subset S\}$.
(iii) $\Longrightarrow$ (ii) follows from I.1.9.c.

PROOF OR THE COROLLARY

If A is an mls in $P(M)$, then, by 1.8, (iv) is satisfied.

I.2.3. PROPOSITION

The following conditions are equivalent for an mls M in S:

(i) *M is an fmls (i.e. is defined on a finite set)*

(ii) *the family M_{MIN} of the minimal sets in M is a pre-mls for M, and consists of finitely many finite sets.*

(iii) *there exists a finite family $\{S_1,\dots,S_n\} \subset S$ that is a pre-mls for M.*

PROOF

(i) $\Longrightarrow$ (iii). Because M is defined on M, some subfamily of P(M) is a pre-mls for M.

(iii) $\Longrightarrow$ (ii) follows from the first past of I.2.2.

(ii) $\Longrightarrow$ (i) follows from I.2.2 (ii) $\Longleftrightarrow$ (iii).

I.2.4. PROPOSITION

Let M *be an fmls in* S, *and* M_{MIN} *the family of minimal sets in* M. *Put* $M = \cup M_{MIN}$. *Then*

(i) $\forall S \in M \exists S' \in M_{MIN} \quad S' \subset S$

(ii) M *is the (minimal) defining set for* M.

(iii) $\{S \in M \mid S \subset M\}$ *is an mls in* P(M) *and a pre-mls in* S.

(iv) *for each* $S \subset M$ *either* $S \in M$ *or* $(M \backslash S) \in M$.

(v) *for each* $S \in M_{MIN}$ *the family* $M_{MIN} \backslash \{S\}$ *is not a pre-mls in* S.

(v) *a subfamily* $M' \subset S$ *is a pre-mls for* M *iff* $M_{MIN} \subset M' \subset M$.

PROOF

(i) follows from I.2.3 (i) $\Longleftrightarrow$ (ii) and I.2.2 (ii) $\Longleftrightarrow$ (iii).

(ii) Clearly M is a defining set for M. Suppose $M' \subset M$ is a proper subset. Choose $S \in M_{MIN}$ such that S meets $M \backslash M'$. Then M' is not a defining set for M, because (a subset of) $M' \cap S$ cannot belong to M, as S is minimal in M.

(iii) Suppose $\{S \in M \mid S \subset M\} \subset M' \in \lambda(P(M))$ and $S \in M' \backslash M$. Then, by (a) and 1.2, $\exists T \in M_{MIN} \quad S \cap T = \emptyset$. This contradicts $T \in M_{MIN} \subset M$!

(iv) follows from (iii).

(v) Because S is minimal, each $T \in M_{MIN} \backslash \{S\}$ meets both S and $M \backslash S$. Hence, by I.1.9.a, $M_{MIN} \backslash \{S\}$ is not a pre-mls.

(vi) follows from (v) and (i) (or (iii)).

We can summarize the results obtained sofar as follows:

I.2.5. THEOREM

We obtain precisely all fmls in S *if we first construct all mls's in* P(M), *for each finite* $M \subset X = \cup S$, *and then add to each mls* M *in* P(M) *those* $S \in S$ *that contain some* $S' \in M$. *In formula*

$$\lambda_f(S) = \bigcup_{M \in P_f(X)} \{\{S \in S \mid S' \in M \quad S' \subset S\} \mid M \in \lambda(P(M))\}.$$

PROOF

This follows from the corollary in I.2.2 combined with I.2.4 (iii).

The following proposition will be useful in many proofs.

I.2.6. PROPOSITION

(a) *If* $\mathcal{A}$ *is a linked system, and* $\cup\mathcal{A}$ *is a finite subset of* X, *then there exists an fmls* $\mathcal{M}$ *in* $\mathcal{S}$ *that contains* $\mathcal{A}$.

(b) *If* $\mathcal{A}$ *is a finite, linked family of subsets of* X, *then there exists an fmls* $\mathcal{M}$, *defined on* $\cup\mathcal{A}$, *such that*

$$\forall A \in \mathcal{A}\, \exists S \in \mathcal{M} \quad S \subset A.$$

REMARK

Observe that (b) is stronger than (a). We did mention (a) because it is more transparant and frequently used.

PROOF

(a) Let $\mathcal{M}'$ be an mls in $P(\cup\mathcal{A})$ that contains $\mathcal{A}$. By I.2.2 (iv) $\Longrightarrow$ (ii) $\mathcal{M}'$ is a pre-mls in $\mathcal{S}$. Put $\mathcal{M} = \underline{\mathcal{M}'}$.

(b) Suppose $\mathcal{A} = \{A_1,\ldots,A_n\}$. Choose $a_{ij} \in A_i \cap A_j$, i,j = 1,...,n, arbitrarily. Apply (a) to the family of $\{a_{ij} \mid j=1,\ldots,n\}$, i = i,...,n.

I.2.7. TYPES OF FMLS'S

We will now formalize the intuitive feeling that the mls $\mathcal{M}$ in P{1,2,3,4,5} and the mls $\mathcal{N}$ in $P\,\mathbb{R}$ ($\mathcal{M}$, $\mathcal{N}$ defined below) have the same structure:

$$\mathcal{M} = \{S \in P\{1,2,3,4,5\} \mid (1 \in S \text{ and } S \cap \{2,3,4\} \neq \emptyset) \text{ or } (S \supset \{2,3,4\})\}$$

$$\mathcal{N} = \{S \in P\mathbb{R} \mid (0 \in S \text{ and } S \cap \{-1,1,6\} \neq \emptyset) \text{ or } (S \supset \{-1,1,6\})\}.$$

Let $\{\mathcal{S}_\alpha \mid \alpha \in J\}$ be the class of families $\mathcal{S}_\alpha$ that satisfy

$$P_f(\cup\mathcal{S}_\alpha) \subset \mathcal{S} \subset P(\cup\mathcal{S}_\alpha)$$

i.e. each S_α contains "all" finite sets. Next let F be the class of all fmls's, i.e.

$$F = \cup\{\lambda_f(S_\alpha) \mid \alpha\in J\}.$$

Let $\alpha,\alpha' \in J$, and suppose M is an fmls in S_α, and M is the minimal defining set for M. If M' satisfies $M \subset M' \subset \cup S_\alpha$, and f: $M' \to \cup S_{\alpha'}$ is arbitrary then it is easily seen that

$$\{f(M'\cap S) \mid S\in M\}$$

is a pre-mls in $S_{\alpha'}$ for

$$\bar{f}(M) \underset{\text{def}}{=} \{S\in S_{\alpha'} \mid f^{-1}(S)\in M\}.$$

It is also easily seen that $\bar{f}(M)$ only depends on M, and on the restriction of f to M. This is an important observation: it reveals that the maximal linkedness of an fmls is preserved under arbitrary mappings, at least between families containing "all" finite sets. Let us look at an example and compare with arbitrary mls's.

EXAMPLES

(a) Let $S = P(\mathbb{R})$ and $T = P_f\mathbb{N}$. Put

$$M_1 = \{S \mid \tfrac{1}{2}\in S\subset\mathbb{R}\}$$

$$M_2 = \{S\subset\mathbb{R} \mid S \text{ contains at least four of the following seven points: } \tfrac{1}{4}, \tfrac{1}{2}, \tfrac{3}{4}, 1,2,3,4\}.$$

Observe that $M_{1,2}$ are mls's, indeed a fixed mls and a 7-mls respectively. Now let e: $\mathbb{R} \to \mathbb{N}$ be the entier-function. Then

$$\bar{e}(M_1) = \{S\in P_f\mathbb{N} \mid e^{-1}S\in M_1\} = \{S \mid 0\in S\in P_f\mathbb{N}\}$$

is again a fixed mls. And

$$\bar{e}(M_2) = \{S\in P_f\mathbb{N} \mid e^{-1}S\in M_2\} = \underline{N}, \quad \text{where}$$

$$N = \{\{0,1\},\{0,2\},\{0,3\},\{0,4\},\{1,2,3,4\}\}$$

is easily seen to be a pre-mls in $P_f\mathbb{N}$.

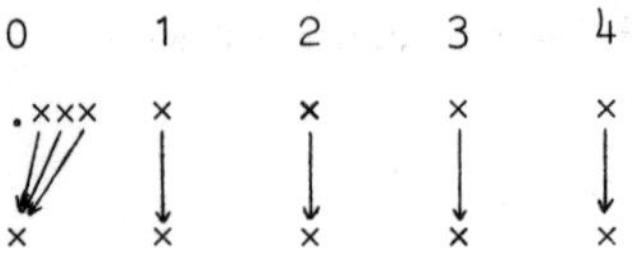

M = "at least four of these seven"

$\bar{e}(M)$ = "either containing 0 and meeting {1,2,3,4}, or containing {1,2,3,4}".

Observe that $\bar{e}M_2$ is an mls, and even a 5-mls.

(b) Let X be the unit circle in the plane, D a diagonal and π: X → D the projection on the diagonal. Let S and T be the families of all intervals in X and D, then $T = \pi S = \{\pi I \mid I \in S\}$. As we saw in I.1.8.a the family

$$M = \{I \in S \mid \text{length } I \geq \pi\}$$

is an mls in S. However, if 0 is the midpoint, and a,b are the endpoints of D, then

$$f(M) = \{fI \mid I \in M\} = \{I \in T \mid 0 \in I \text{ and either a or b} \in I\}$$

clearly is not a pre-mls in T. It is contained e.g. in both mls's $\{I \mid 0 \in I \in T\}$ and $\{I \in T \mid I$ contains at least two points of 0,a,b$\}$.

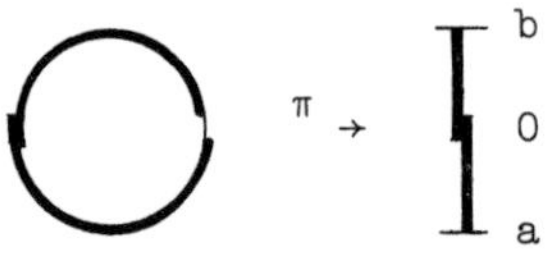

REMARK

Under suitable conditions on the families S and T also arbitrary mls's are "preserved" (as mls's) under maps $\cup S \to \cup T$. This is the subject of II.4.

I.2.8.

Let M, N be two fmls's, with minimal defining sets M and N. Then we say that M and N have the same *type*, in notation:

$$\text{type } M = \text{type } N$$

if there exists a bijection f: N → M such that

$$M = \bar{f}(N).$$

We say that

$$\text{type } M < \text{type } N$$

if there exists a function $f: N \to M$ which is not 1-1 and satisfies

$$M = \bar{f}(N).$$

Moreover we write "type $M \leq$ type N" for "type $M <$ type N or type $M = N$".

In this way we obtain an equivalence relation on the class F of all fmls's, and a partial order on the set of equivalence classes, as is easily checked. Let C be such an equivalence class. Clearly all $M \in C$ are n-mls's for the same n. For this n we can also find in C an mls in the powerset of $\{1,\ldots,n\}$, which can be taken as representation of C. Because there are only finitely many mls's on $\{1,\ldots,n\}$, there are only countably many equivalence classes.

Let us now turn to the partial order of the set of equivalence classes. The following facts are simple to prove.

I.2.9.

(a) *If* M *is an* m*-mls, and* N *an* n*-mls, then* type $M <$ type N *implies* $m < n$.

(b) *For each* m*-mls* M *there exists an* (m+1)*-mls* M' *such that*

$$\text{type } M < \text{type } M'.$$

(c) *Each maximal linearly ordered set of types has the ordertype of the natural numbers.*

(d) *For each two fmls's* M *and* M' *there exists fmls's* N *and* N' *such that*

$$\text{type } N' \leq \text{type } M \leq \text{type } N$$

and $\quad \text{type } N' \leq \text{type } M' \leq \text{type } N.$

We can even choose N' *maximal and* N *minimal as follows from* (c). *However these maximal* N' *and minimal* N *are not at all uniquely determined by* M *and* M' *(see figure at p. 26).*

PROOF

(a) is trivial.

(b) Let $\mathcal{M}$ be defined on M. Define a surjection f: {1,...,m+1} → M. Let $\mathcal{M}'$ be any mls in P{1,...,m+1} containing $\{f^{-1}S \mid S \in \mathcal{M}\}$.

(c) is trivial from (a) and (b).

(d) Since all fixed mls's have the same type and this type precedes all other types, we only have to construct $\mathcal{N}$. As we may replace $\mathcal{M}$ and $\mathcal{M}'$

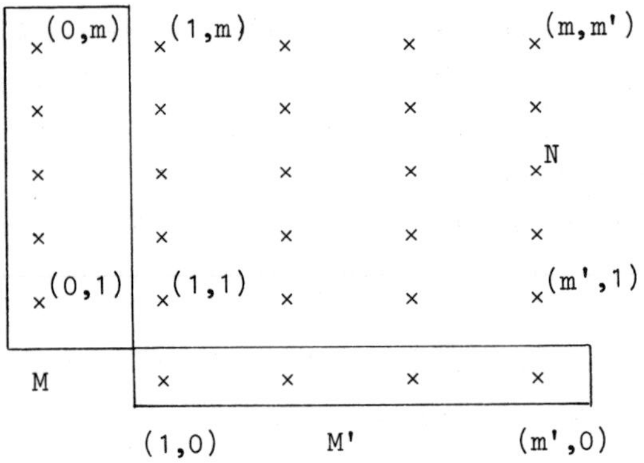

by mls's of the same type, we may suppose that their defining sets are

M = {(0,1),...,(0,m)}

and

M' = {(1,0),...,(m',0)}

respectively, and moreover $\cup\mathcal{M}$ = M, $\cup\mathcal{M}'$ = M'. Put N = {1,...,m'} × {1,...,m}, and let π_1: N → M' and π_2: N → M be the projection maps. Let $\mathcal{N}$ be any mls in P(N) which contains all sets $\pi_1^{-1}S'$ and $\pi_2^{-1}S$, for $S' \in \mathcal{M}'$, $S \in \mathcal{M}$. Then $\bar{\pi}_1(\mathcal{N}) = \mathcal{M}'$ and $\bar{\pi}_2(\mathcal{N}) = \mathcal{M}$. Thus indeed type $\mathcal{M} \leqq$ type $\mathcal{N}$ and type $\mathcal{M}' \leqq$ type $\mathcal{N}$.

I.2.10. EXAMPLES (we use the notational conventions from page 27).

First we describe all types of n-mls for n ≤ 5 and some for n = 6, simply by giving for each type (n,i) a pre-mls in P_n. It is easily seen that all given pre-mls correspond to mls's of different types. From the fact that t(0,1,2,3,4,5) = (1,1,0,1,1,4) (proved in I.3.8) it follows that indeed all types (n,i) with n ≤ 5 are described.

Let us explain the notation below by means of two examples:

type (4,1) is represented by the pre-mls {{1,2},{1,3},{1,4},{2,3,4}}.
type (5,2) is represented by the pre-mls {{1,2}} ∪ {all three-point-sets in P_5 that contain either 1 or (exclusively) 2}.

The word (scheme) near the figure means that not all minimal sets are indicated but only a "representative" selection. The sets which are "representative", and should be copied in order to obtain all minimal sets (copied, by taking certain permutations of {1,...,n}) are indicated by dashed lines. So is in type (5,2) the set {1,3,4} "representative" for "all three-point-sets in P_5 that contain either 1 or 2".

For the definition of case (k), $-2 \leq k \leq n-1$, see I.3.6.

type	minimal sets	figure	number of mls's of this type in $P_n = P\{1,...,n\}$
type (1,1) (case(-2))	1 ×	 (fixed mls)	n
type (2,)	does not	exist	
type (3,1) (case(-1))	1 2 3 × × × × × × ×	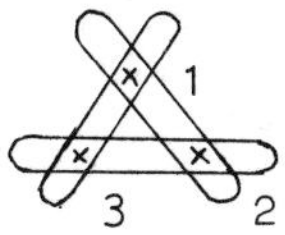	$\binom{n}{3}$
type (4,1) (case (3))	1 2 3 4 × × × × × × × × ×	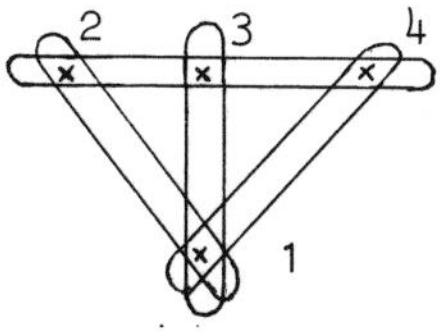	$n\binom{n-1}{3}$

type (5,1)
(case (0))
	1 2 3 4 5
	× × ×
	× × ×
	× × ×
	× × ×
	× × ×
	× × ×
	   × × ×
	   × × ×
	   × × ×
	     × × ×
		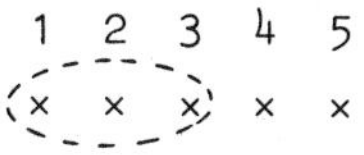
		(scheme)
			$\binom{n}{5}$

type	minimal sets	figure	number of mls's of this type in P_n

type (5,2) (case (1))

1	2	3	4	5
×	×			
×		×	×	
×		×		×
×			×	×
	×	×	×	
	×	×		×
	×		×	×

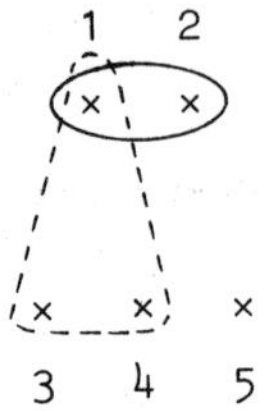

(scheme)

$\binom{n}{2}\binom{n-2}{3}$

type (5,3) (case (2))

1	2	3	4	5
×	×			
×		×		
×			×	×
	×	×	×	
	×	×		×

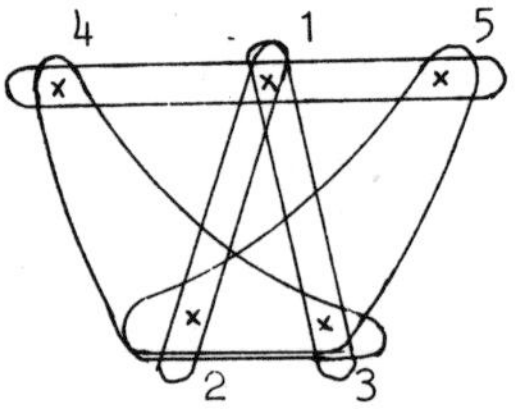

$n\binom{n-1}{2}\binom{n-3}{2}$

type (5,4) (case (4))

1	2	3	4	5
×	×			
×		×		
×			×	
×				×
	×	×	×	×

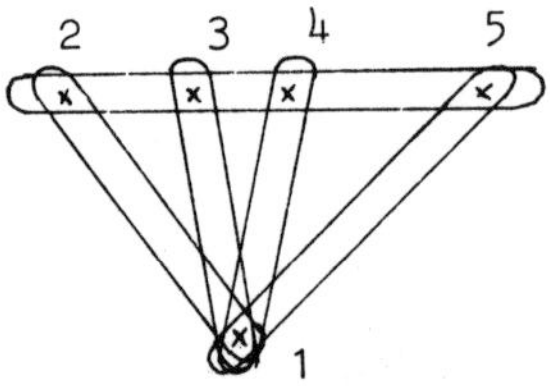

$n\binom{n-1}{4}$

type (6,1) (case (5))

1	2	3	4	5	6
×	×				
×		×			
×			×		
×				×	
×					×
	×	×	×	×	×

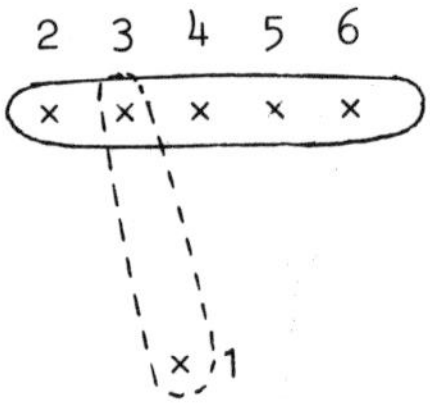

(scheme)

$n\binom{n-1}{5}$

type (6,2) (case (3))

1	2	3	4	5	6
×	×				
×		×			
×			×		
×				×	×
	×	×	×	×	
	×	×	×		×

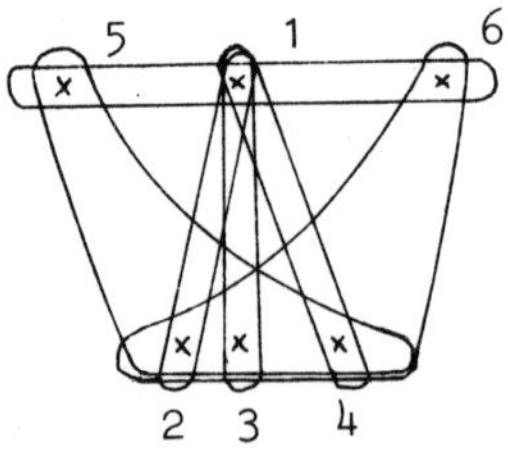

$n\binom{n-1}{3}\binom{n-4}{2}$

type	minimal sets						figure	number of mls's of this type in P_n
	1	2	3	4	5	6		
type (6,3)	×	×					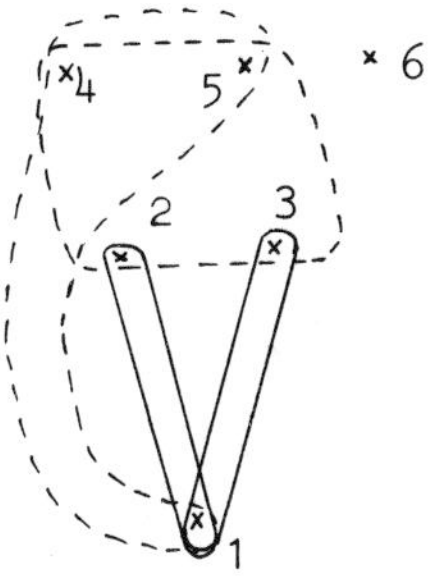	$n\binom{n-1}{2}\binom{n-3}{3}$
(case (2))	×		×					
	×			×	×			
	×			×		×		
	×				×	×		
		×	×	×	×			
		×	×	×		×		
		×	×		×	×	(scheme)	
	1	2	3	4	5	6		
type (6,4)	×	×	×				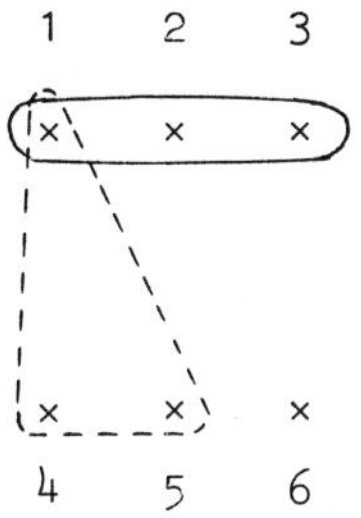	$\binom{n}{3}\binom{n-3}{3}$
(case (3))	×			×	×			
	×			×		×		
	×				×	×		
		×		×	×			
		×		×		×		
		×			×	×	(scheme)	
			×	×	×			
			×	×		×		
			×		×	×		
	1	2	3	4	5	6		
type (6,5)	×	×					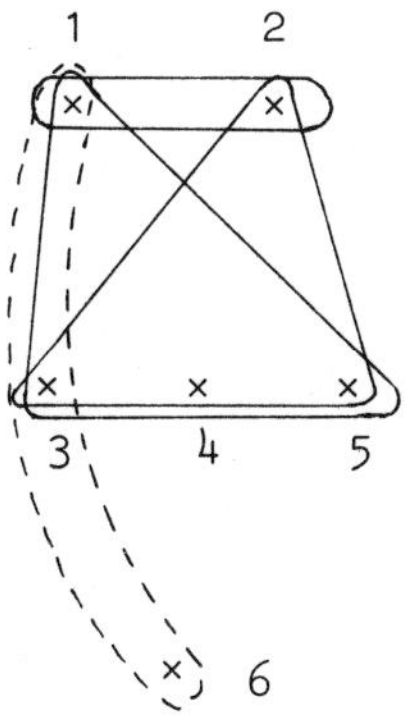	$n\binom{n-1}{2}\binom{n-3}{3}$
(case (1))	×		×	×	×			
	×		×			×		
	×			×		×		
	×				×	×		
		×	×	×	×			
		×	×			×		
		×		×		×		
		×			×	×		

Next we indicate the partial ordering between the types defined above. Below the dots indicate types, and a line between the dot = type (i,j) and the dot(i+1,j') symbolizes that type (i,j) < type(i+1,j'). Such an inequality is proved by exhibition of a certain function $f: \{1,\dots,i+1\} \xrightarrow{\text{onto}} \{1,\dots,i\}$ (see I.2.8). This function identifies just one pair, say k,k', in {1,...,i+1}. This is indicated by writing k ~ k' next to the line.

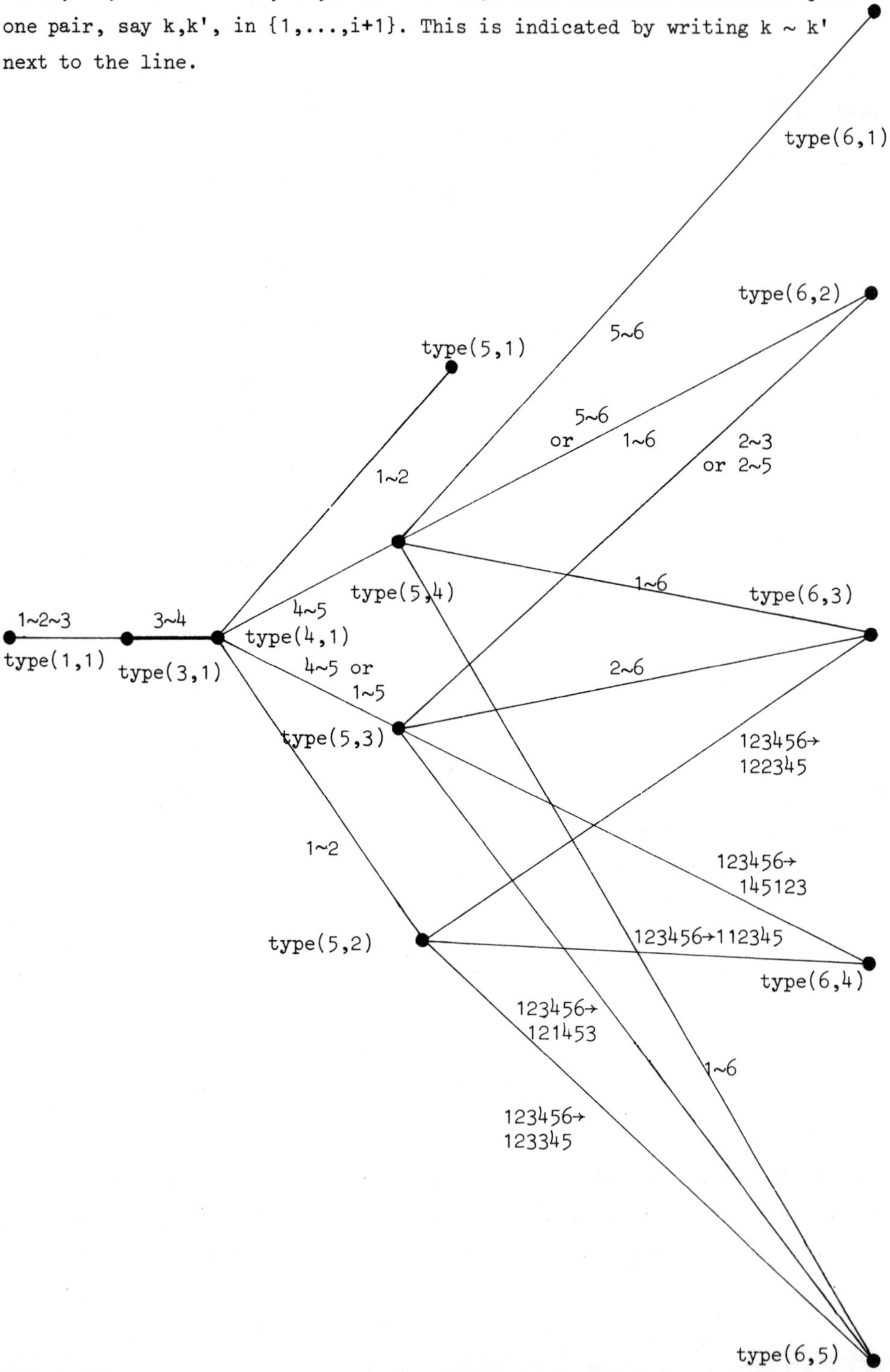

I.3. COUNTING MLS'S

I.3.1.

Numerical results dominate this section. In particular we compute the number $\lambda(n)$ of mls's in the powerset of an n-point-set for $n \leq 7$. I.e. for $n = 7$ an algorithm will be given which has been implemented by A.E. Brouwer on a PDP-8 computer for the calculation of $\lambda(7)$ (and of $\lambda(1),\ldots,\lambda(6)$) and another, much more efficient, method, also of A.E. Brouwer, is used to evaluate $\lambda(n)$ by hand for $n \leq 6$. (These $\lambda(1),\ldots,\lambda(6)$ had been evaluated by G.A. Jensen already in 1966). Moreover we show that all types of n-mls's for $n \leq 5$ have been exhibited in the list in I.2.10.

First we need some notational conventions for the rest of this section.

$P_n = P\{1,\ldots,n\}$ is the powerset of an n-point-set.

HP_n = "half of P_n" = $\{S \in P_n \mid 1 \leq \text{card } S < \frac{n}{2}\} \cup$

$\cup$ one of each pair of complementary $\frac{n}{2}$ -point-sets (if n is even), arbitrarily choosen.

$S^c = \{1,\ldots,n\} \setminus S$ for $S \in P_n$ (if n is obvious from the context).

$\lambda(n) = \text{card } \lambda(P_n)$ = the number of mls's in the powerset of an n-point-set.

$t(n)$ = the number of different types of n-mls's.

We will denote the different types of n-mls's by

type(n,1),type(n,2),...,type(n,t(n))

in an arbitrary order (as there is no "natural" order). For the definition of type(i,j) for $i \leq 5$ and $j \leq t(i)$ and for $i = 6$ and $j \leq 5$, see page 23.

I.3.2. n-MLS'S FOR $n \leq 3$

Recall the definition of an n-mls:
An mls $\mathcal{M}$ is an n-mls if there exists an n-point set M, but no smaller set, such that

$$\forall S \in \mathcal{M}\ \exists S' \in M \quad S' \subset S \quad \text{and} \quad S' \in \mathcal{M}.$$

As an immediate consequence any 1-mls is fixed and $\lambda(1) = 1$, and also any fixed mls is a 1-mls. Hence n-mls's with $n > 1$ are free.

Next suppose M is an mls in $P_2 = \{\emptyset,\{1\},\{2\},\{1,2\}\}$ but not the fixed mls of all sets containing 1. Then $\{1\} \notin M$ so $\exists S \in M \quad S \cap \{1\} = \emptyset$. Only $S = \{2\}$ is disjoint of $\{1\}$, so M is the fixed mls of all sets containing 2. Consequently $\lambda(2) = 2$ and there is no (free) 2-mls.

If M is a free mls in P_3 then M contains no singletons so $M \subset \{\{1,2\},\{1,3\},\{2,3\},\{1,2,3\}\}$. However the latter family is linked and thus equals M because of the maximality of M. Hence there is precisely one free mls in P_3, and precisely one type of 3-mls's. As there are 3 fixed mls's in P_3 (n fixed mls's in P_n for each n) $\lambda(3) = 4$.

The next lemmas are crucial for the computation of $\lambda(n)$ for $n \geq 4$, and for the - extremely rough - estimates we have for $\lambda(n)$. The first is a modification of I.1.11.b, so that we may omit its simple proof.

I.3.3. LEMMA

If F *is a finite set and* $M \subset$ PF *is linked then* M *is an mls (in* PF*) iff*

$$\forall F' \subset F \quad F' \in M \quad \textit{or (exclusively)} \quad F \backslash F' \in M.$$

I.3.4.

Consider all $2^{n-1}-1$ pairs of complementary proper subsets of $\{1,\ldots,n\}$. Then, by the above lemma, an mls M in P_n is a linked subfamily of P_n which contains precisely one set of each pair. Consequently

$$\lambda(n) \leq 2^{2^{n-1}-1}.$$

Next we may represent such pair by its element that belongs to HP_n, roughly speaking, by its smallest set. Thus we may represent $M \in \lambda P_n$ by a subfamily M' as follows:

$$M \in \lambda P_n \qquad\qquad M' \subset HP_n$$

$$M \longrightarrow M \cap HP_n = M'$$

$$M' \cup \{S \in P_n \backslash HP_n \mid S^c \notin M'\} \longleftarrow M'$$

We may still go further and represent M by only those sets in $M \cap HP_n$ that are $\subset$-minimal. We denote this representation by ϕ:

$$\lambda P_n \xrightarrow{\phi} P(HP_n)$$

$$M \xmapsto{\phi} \phi(M) = M_{MIN} \cap HP_n.$$

Recall that M_{MIN} is the smallest pre-mls for M (see I.2.4 (v)), so $M_{MIN} \cap HP_n$ does, in general, not determine M in the sense that M is the only mls containing this family. Yet we just made it plausible that ϕ is 1-1. This is worked out and formalized in the following lemma, the major importance of which lies in the characterization of the image of ϕ. This enables us to count $\lambda(n)$ by counting down $\phi(\lambda P_n)$ which is much easier (i.e. is doable for $n \leq 7$) than counting λP_n (which is not doable for $n \geq 5$). This because $\phi(\lambda P_n)$ has much more symmetries than λP_n.

LEMMA

If ϕ: $\lambda P_n \to P(HP_n)$ *is defined by*

$$\phi(M) = M_{MIN} \cap HP_n$$

then ϕ *is* 1-1.
If $M' \in P(HP_n)$ *then* $M' = \phi(M)$ *for some* $M \in \lambda P_n$ *iff* M' *is linked and no* $S \in M'$ *contains a* $T \in M'\backslash\{S\}$ *(i.e.* M' *is an* $\subset$*-anti-chain).*

The straightforward but tedious formal proof is only given for the sake of completeness, but can easily be skipped by the reader.

PROOF

Suppose M, M' are two different mls's in P_n, and yet $\phi M = \phi M' =$ $= M_{MIN} \cap HP_n = M'_{MIN} \cap HP_n$. Because M_{MIN} is a pre-mls for M, $\exists S \in M_{MIN}\backslash M'$. Hence $S \notin HP_n$, i.e. $S^c \in HP_n$. Also $S^c \in M'$. Let T be a minimal set of M', contained in S^c, then, by definition of HP_n, $T \in HP_n$, so $T \in M'_{MIN} \cap HP_n$. Consequently $T \in M_{MIN} \subset M$, contradictory to $T \cap S = \emptyset$. This shows that ϕ is 1-1.

The "only if" part of the second assumption is trivial. The proof of the if part proceeds as follows: first we define

$$P(HP_n) \xrightarrow{\psi_1} P(HP_n) \xrightarrow{\psi_2} P(P_n)$$

by

$$\psi_1(M_1) = \{S \in HP_n \mid \exists T \in M_1 \quad T \subset S\} \qquad M_1 \subset HP_n$$

$$\psi_2(M_2) = M_2 \cup \{S \in P_n \setminus HP_n \mid S^c \notin M_2\} \qquad M_2 \subset HP_n$$

Next we observe that $\forall M_{1,2} \subset HP_n$

(i) If M_1 is linked then $\psi_1 M_1$ is linked.

(ii) If $\psi_1 M_1$ is linked then $\psi_2 \psi_1 M_1$ is linked.

(iii) $\psi_2 M_2$ contains precisely one of each pair of complementary subsets of $\{1,\ldots,n\}$.

Combination of (i), (ii), (iii) (with $M_2 = \phi_1 M_1$) and I.3.3 shows that if M_1 is linked then $\psi_2\psi_1 M_1$ is an mls in P_n. Finally we claim that if also no set of M_1 contains another (i.e. $M_1 = M_{1MIN}$) then $\phi\psi_2\psi_1 M_1 = M_1$. For

$$\phi\psi_2\psi_1 M_1 = (\psi_2\psi_1 M_1)_{MIN} \cap HP_n =$$

$$= (\psi_2\psi_1 M_1 \cap HP_n)_{MIN} =$$

$$= (\psi_1 M_1)_{MIN} = M_{1MIN} = M_1.$$

As immediate corollary we have

I.3.5. THEOREM

The number $\lambda(n)$ *of mls's in the powerset of an n-points set is equal to the number of linked subfamilies of* HP_n *that are* $\subset$*-anti-chains.*

One more lemma is needed before we attack $\lambda(4)$, $\lambda(5)$ and $\lambda(6)$. For we will classify the mls's in P_4, P_5 and P_6 according to the number of two-point-sets they contain. How these two-point-sets are situated is described now.

I.3.6. LEMMA

If $M \in \lambda P_n$ *then precisely one of the following cases holds:*

case(-2): M *is fixed (i.e.* M *is an 1-mls),*

case(-1): M *is a 3-mls,*

case(k): M contains k *two-point-sets which have one point in common (if* $k \geq 2$*)* (k=0,1,2,...,n-1)

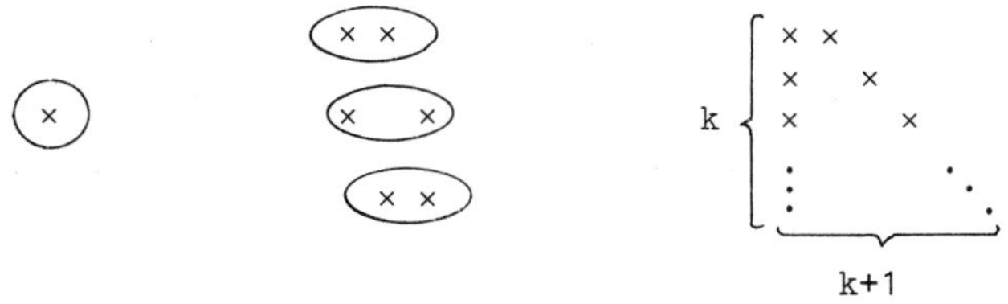

case(-2) case(-1) case(k), $k \geq 0$.

PROOF

Suppose M is not fixed (i.e. contains no singletons) and M contains at least 3 two-point-sets, say A, B and C (if this is not satisfied then we are obviously in case(-2), case(0), case(1) or case(2)). Now $A \cap B \neq \emptyset$, $A \cap C \neq \emptyset$ and $B \cap C \neq \emptyset$. If $A \cap B \cap C = \emptyset$, then $A \cup B \cup C$ must be a three-point-set and $\{A,B,C\}$ obviously is a pre-mls, i.e. we are in case(-1). Else $\exists x \in A \cap B \cap C$. Now if M contains other two-point-sets, say D, then we claim that also $x \in D$. For suppose $x \notin D$. Because $D \cap A$, $D \cap B$, and $D \cap C$ are nonempty, but $A \setminus \{x\}$, $B \setminus \{x\}$ and $C \setminus \{x\}$ are disjoint (singletons), D cannot be a two-point-set.

Finally observe that k cannot be larger than n-1. This proves the lemma.

I.3.7.

Computation of $\lambda(4)$, $\lambda(5)$ *and* $\lambda(6)$.

Let $l(n,k)$ denote the number of mls's in P_n in case(k), $(-2 \leq k \leq n-1)$. Obviously

$$l(n,-2) = n \quad \text{and} \quad l(n,-1) = \binom{n}{3}$$

because a 3-mls is determined by the choice of its smallest defining set, which has 3 points.
For $k \geq 0$ $l(n,k)$ is the number of linked anti-chains in HP_n for which the number of two-point-sets is k, while for $k > 2$ the two-element-sets must have one point in common. So for $n \geq 3$

$$\lambda(n) = n + \binom{n}{3} + l(n,0) + \ldots + l(n,n-1).$$

n = 4

Observe that there are $\binom{4}{2} = 6$ two-point-sets in P_4, so 3 pairs of complementary two-point-sets. Consequently each $M \in \lambda P_4$ contains precisely three two-point-sets, i.e. $l(4,0) = l(4,1) = 0$. There are precisely 4 anti-chains with precisely 3 two-point-sets having one point in common, viz. with intersection 1, 2, 3 and 4:

$\{\{1,2\},\{1,3\},\{1,4\}\}$ (see figure)

$\{\{2,1\},\{2,3\},\{2,4\}\}$,

$\{\{3,1\},\{3,2\},\{3,4\}\}$,

and $\{\{4,1\},\{4,2\},\{4,3\}\}$.

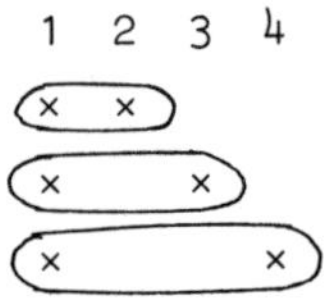

Hence

$$\lambda(4,3) = 4$$

and

$$\lambda(4) = 4 + 4 + 0 + 0 + 4 = 12.$$

The mls in case(3) corresponding to the first mentioned anti-chain is given by its minimal sets:

$\{\{1,2\},\{1,3\},\{1,4\},\{2,3,4\}\}$

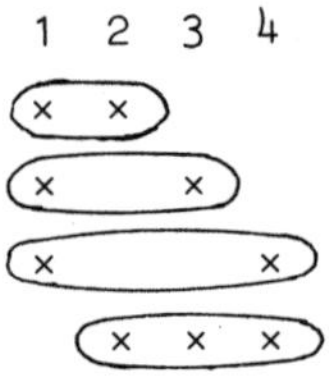

It is easily seen that the other mls's can be obtained from this mls by permutations, i.e. are of the same type. Thus $t(4) = 1$.

n = 5

$HP_5 = \{S \subset \{1,\ldots,5\} \mid S \text{ has 1 or 2 points}\}$, but for case (0), ..., case(4) we only count linked anti-chains which do not contain singletons, i.e. linked anti-chains in the family $\{S \subset \{1,\ldots,5\} \mid S \text{ has 2 points}\}$.

The case (0).
There is precisely one linked anti-chain in this family without two-point-sets, viz. the empty subfamily. Thus

$$l(5,0) = 1.$$

To this anti-chain corresponds the mls consisting of all 3, 4 and 5-point-sets in P_5.

The case (1).
There are $\binom{5}{2} = 10$ two-point-sets in P_5, so

$$l(5,1) = 10.$$

The case (k) for $2 \leq k \leq 4$.
There are $5\binom{4}{k}$ ways to select k two-point-sets in 1,2,3,4,5 that have one point in common. I.e.

$$l(5,k) = 5\binom{4}{k}.$$

For fixed k the corresponding mls's are obviously of the same type, so there are 5 different types of mls's, each corresponding to one of the cases (0)-(4). For k = 3 we have a 4-mls, the other k must give 5-mls's, because there are only 3 types of n-mls's for n < 5 (viz. n = 1, 3 and 4), which correspond to k = -2, -1 and 3. So t(5) = 4. Moreover

$$\lambda(5) = l(n,-2) + l(n,-1) + l(n,0) + l(n,1) + l(n,2) + l(n,3) + l(n,4) =$$

$$= 5 + 10 + 1 + 10 + 5\binom{4}{2} + 5\binom{4}{3} + 5\binom{4}{4} =$$

$$= 81.$$

n = 6

HP_6 consists of all singletons, and all two-point-sets and one set of each of the $\binom{6}{3}/2 = 10$ pairs of complementary three-point-sets, say all three-point-sets containing the point 1.

Case (0).
Observe that all three-point-sets in HP_6 meet each other. So the linked anti-chains in HP_6 not containing singletons or two-point-sets are the arbitrary families of the three-point-sets in HP_6. Thus

$$l(6,0) = 2^{10} = 1024.$$

Case (1).
Suppose $C \subset HP_6$ is an anti-chain an $\{1,2\} \in C$ is the only two-point-set in C. Then C cannot contain any three-point-set containing {1,2}, because C is an anti-chain On the other hand any three-point-set in HP_6

1	2	3	4	5	6
×	×				
×	o	×	×	o	o
×	o	×	o	×	o
×	o	×	o	o	×
×	o	o	×	×	o
×	o	o	×	o	×
×	o	o	o	×	×

meets {1,2}, viz. in the point 1. This implies that its complements also meets {1,2}, viz. in the point 2. There are $\binom{4}{2} = 6$ pairs of complementary three-point-sets, both of which meet {1,2}. Again three-point-sets that are not complementary, meet each other. This gives 2^6 linked anti-chains containing {1,2} as only two-point-set and $\binom{6}{2}\, 2^6 = 960$ linked anti-chains with precisely one two-point-set:

$$l(6,1) = 960.$$

Case (2).

Suppose the linked anti-chain $C \subset HP_6$ contains {1,2},{1,3} but no other two-point-sets. As the three-point-sets in HP_6 are the three-point-sets in P_6 that contain 1, the three-point-sets in HP_6 that meet both {1,2} and {1,3} but contain neither of them, are {1,4,5}, {1,4,6} and {1,5,6}. So there are 2^3 linked anti-chains in HP_6 with {1,2} and {1,3} as only two-point-sets, and $6\binom{5}{2}\, 2^3 = 480$ anti-chains with two two-point-sets:

1	2	3	4	5	6
×	×				
×		×			
×	o	o	×	×	o
×	o	o	×	o	×
×	o	o	o	×	×

$$\lambda(6,2) = 480.$$

Case (3).

Suppose the linked anti-chain $C \subset HP_6$ contains {1,2}, {1,3} and {1,4} but no other two-point-set. The only three-point-set in HP_6 that meets these sets but contains neither of them is {1,5,6}. This gives two linked anti-chains in HP_6, viz. {1,2},{1,3},{1,4} and {1,2},{1,3},{1,4},{1,5,6}. Hence there are $6\binom{5}{3}\, 2 = 120$ linked anti-chains with precisely 3 two-point-sets in case (3):

1	2	3	4	5	6
×	×				
×		×			
×			×		
×	o	o	o	×	×

$$l(6,3) = 120.$$

In Case (4) and (5) the possible linked anti-chains can consist of 2-element-sets only. So

$$l(6,4) = 6\binom{5}{4} = 30$$

and

$$l(6,5) = 6.$$

Thus

$$\lambda(6) = \lambda(-2) + \lambda(-1) + \lambda(0) + \lambda(1) + \lambda(2) + \lambda(3) + \lambda(4) + \lambda(5) =$$

$$= 6 + 20 + 1024 + 960 + 480 + 120 + 30 + 6 = 2646.$$

For $n = 6$ almost 3/4 of all mls's belong to case (0) or case (1). We generalize as follows: for even n there are

(a) $$2^{\binom{n}{n/2}/2} = 2^{\binom{n-1}{n/2-1}}$$

anti-chains in HP_n consisting of n/2-point-sets only. For odd n there are

(b) $$2^{\binom{n-1}{n/2-3/2}}$$

linked anti-chains in the family $A = \{A, S_n\setminus A \mid 1\in A \text{ and } A \text{ has } [n/2] \text{ points}\}$. Note that only complementary sets in A are disjoint. Next we see easily:

(c) $l(n,-2) = n$ $(\forall n)$

(d) $l(n,-1) = \binom{n}{3}$ $(n\geq 3)$

(e) $l(n,k) \geq n\binom{n-1}{k} \sum_{i=2}^{k-1} 2^{\binom{n-k-1}{i}}$ $(n/2\leq k\leq n-3)$

(f) $l(n,n-5) = n\binom{n-1}{4}\ 114$ $(n\geq 10)$

(g) $l(n,n-4) = n\binom{n-1}{3}\ (2^3+1)$ $(n\geq 8)$

(h) $l(n,n-3) = n\binom{n-1}{2}\ (2^0+1)$ $(n\geq 6)$

(i) $l(n,n-2) = n(n-1)$ $(n\geq 5)$

(j) $l(n,n-1) = n$ $(n\geq 4)$

Here (e) is obtained by considering for $i = 2,3,\dots,n-k-1$ anti-chains with k two-point-sets and furthermore only (i+1)-point-sets.
The equations (a) – (j) give us a lower bound for $\lambda(n)$. The upper bound given in I.3.7 can be sharpened a little e.g. by observing that there are only n mls's that contain a singleton. The other mls's correspond to linked anti-chains in $HP_n\setminus\{\emptyset,\{1\},\dots,\{n\}\}$, so

(k) $\lambda(n) \leq 2^{2^{n-1}-1-n} + n$ $(n\geq 2)$.

A different upper bound can be obtained as follows. Put $P_n = \{S \subset S_n \mid n \in S\} \cup \cup \{S \subset S_n \mid n \notin S\}$. Then the maps $\lambda P_n \to P\{S \mid n \in S \in S_n\}$ defined by $M \to \{S \in M \mid n \notin S\}$ and $M \to \{S \in M \mid n \notin S\}_{MIN}$ are 1-1. (For the first map recall that an mls contains precisely one of each pair of complementary subsets.) Now the second map maps M onto an anti-chain in S_{n-1}. Let us denote the *number of non-empty anti-chains* in S_n by $\alpha(n)$. Then we just proved:

(1) $\qquad \lambda(n) \leq \alpha(n-1).$

In [12] Kleitman showed that

(m) $\qquad {}^2\log \alpha(n) \sim \binom{n}{[n/2]} \qquad$ (where f~g means lim f/g→1).

Combination of a, b, 1 and m yields the following

THEOREM

(n) $\qquad {}^2\log \lambda(n) \sim {}^2\log \alpha(n-1) \sim \binom{n}{[n/2]} \sim 2^n/\sqrt{2\pi n}.$

For more details and an estimation of the ${}^2\log$ of the number of all linked systems in P_n, see [2]. Let us now compare some numerical values.

n	$\lambda(n)$	$\alpha(n-1)$	${}^2\log \lambda(n)$	${}^2\log \alpha(n-1)$	$\frac{2^n}{\sqrt{2\pi(n-1)}}$	$\frac{2^n}{\sqrt{2\pi n}}$	$\binom{n-1}{[n/2]-1}$
0	1	-	0	-	-	∞	-
1	1	1	0	0	∞	0.798	0
2	2	2	1	1	1.596	1.128	1
3	4	5	2	2.322	2.257	1.843	2
4	12	19	3.585	4.248	3.685	3.192	3
5	81	167	6.340	7.384	6.383	5.709	6
6	2646	7580	11.370	12.888	11.418	10.424	10
7	1422564	7828353	20.440	22.900	20.847	19.301	20
	conjectured:						
8	$7\times10^{10}<\lambda(8)<4\times10^{11}<\alpha(7)<4\times10^{12}$				38.601	36.108	35
9	$10^{21}<\lambda(9)<5\times10^{21}<\alpha(8)<10^{24}$				72.216	68.086	70

Here $\lambda(7)$, $\alpha(5)$ and $\alpha(6)$ (and also all other values for control) have been computed by A.E. Brouwer on a PDP-8 computer. The algorithm used for λ is described below. As this was done only once, we cannot be absolutely sure of all values. Esp. $\lambda(7)$ seems a little low, if we compare ${}^2\log \lambda(n) - 2^n/\sqrt{2\pi(n-1)}$ for n = 1,3,4,5,6 with n = 7: $2^{20.84} \approx 1.88\times10^6$.

I.3.8. ALGORITHM FOR THE COMPUTATION OF $\lambda(n)$

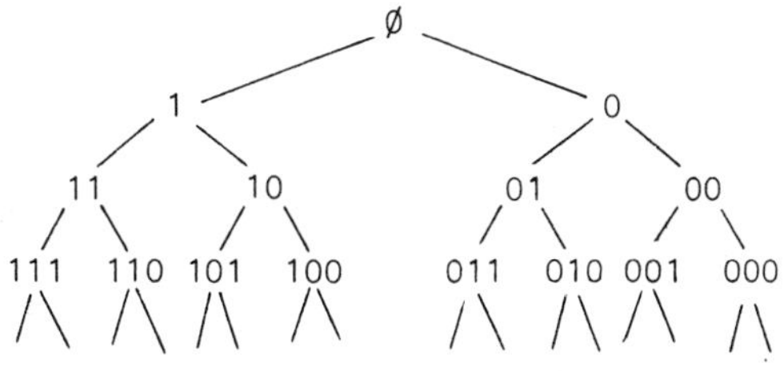

Let Γ be the tree of all sequences of 0's or 1's of length $\leq$ n-1, such that the empty sequence is at the top and the sequences of length n-1 are the roots, and each sequence $(i_1,\ldots,i_k)$ is connected to above only with the sequence $(i_1,\ldots,i_{k-1})$ (if $k>0$), and to below with the sequences $(i_1,\ldots,i_k,0)$ (on the right) and $(i_1,\ldots,i_k,1)$ (on the left) (if $k<n-1$). We make a correspondence between the sequences and certain families of subsets (including all mls's) of $\{1,\ldots,n\}$ in the following way: we denumerate the pairs of proper, complementary subsets of $\{1,\ldots,n\}$:

$$(S_1^0,S_1^1),\ldots,(S^0_{2^{n-1}-1},S^1_{2^{n-1}-1}).$$

Thus

$$S_i^0 \cup S_i^1 = \{1,\ldots,n\}$$

and

$$S_i^0 \cap S_i^1 = \emptyset \qquad \text{for } i = 1,\ldots,2^{n-1}-1.$$

Then we let $(i_1,\ldots,i_k)$ correspond to

$$\{S_1^{i_1},S_2^{i_2},\ldots,S_k^{i_k}\}.$$

We say that a sequence $(i_1,\ldots,i_k)$ is linked if the corresponding family is linked. Then, according to I.3.6, the mls's in P_n just correspond 1-1 to the linked sequences of length n-1.

Now our game consists in starting in the top of the tree, and moving through the tree from one linked sequence to another sequence (following strict rules) until we reach the top for the second time. Our game is such that we shall come to each root that corresponds to an mls (= to an (n-1)-sequence that is linked) just once. So if we count the number of times we reach the lowest level, then at the end we find $\lambda(n)$. We start in $\emptyset$, by going down. Going down:

If we are in the sequence $(i_1,\ldots,i_k)$ $0 \leq k \leq n-1$ and $k = n-1$, then we are in the lowest level, we have found another mls and go up. If $k < n-1$, then we check whether $(i_1,\ldots,i_k,0)$ is a linked sequence or not. In the former case we move to this sequence and go down again. Else $(i_1,\ldots,i_k,1)$ must be linked, so we go to this sequence and go down again. Going up:

If we are in $(i_1,\ldots,i_k)$, $0 \leq k \leq n-1$ and $k = 0$ and we came from 1, then we are ready. Else we go to 1 and go down. If $k > 0$, then we look at i_k. If $i_k = 1$, or if $(i_1,\ldots,i_{k-1},1)$ is not linked, then we go to $(i_1,\ldots,i_{k-1})$ where we go up again. If $i_k = 0$ and $(i_1,\ldots,i_{k-1},1)$ is linked, then we go to $(i_1,\ldots,i_{k-1},1)$ and we go down again.

It is easily seen that in this way we move through all linked sequences of the tree, with a preference for going down and going - in the figure - to the left; but with a prohibition to go twice to the same maximal linked sequence.

I.4. MLS'S IN FAMILIES OF FINITE SETS

Let X be any set and

$$\mathcal{S} = P_f X$$

is the family of all finite subsets of X. The main result of this section will be that for any mls $\mathcal{M}$ in $\mathcal{S}$ the family $\mathcal{M}_{MIN}$, which necessarily is a pre-mls, is finite or countable. Of course this will also be true for those mls's in an arbitrary family $\mathcal{T}$ that have a defining set M satisfying

$$P_f(M) \subset \mathcal{T},$$

if each set of the mls contains a finite set, belonging to the mls.

A similar theorem is conjectured (cf. V.3) if $\mathcal{S}$ is the family of all closed sets in a compact space. Then for any $\mathcal{M} \in \lambda(\mathcal{S})$ also $\mathcal{M}_{MIN}$ is a pre-mls, and it is conjectured that $\cup\mathcal{M}_{MIN}$ has a σ-compact dense subset. If this is true, it does require a proof quite different from the purely combinatorial proof that is given in this section. In this case $\mathcal{M}_{MIN}$ of course need not be countable: see I.1.3(d) and I.1.8(b).

I.4.1. THEOREM

Let X *be a set and* M *an mls in* $S = P_f(X)$. *Then*

(a) $\forall S \in M\ \exists S' \in M_{MIN}\quad S' \subset S$. *Hence* M_{MIN} *is a pre-mls for* M.

(b) *For each natural number* k, M_{MIN} *contains only finitely many sets of* k *points. Hence* M_{MIN} *is finite or countable.*

(c) M *is an fmls iff* M_{MIN} *is finite.*

(d) *For each natural number* k *there exists a finite subfamily* $M(k) \subset M_{MIN}$ *such that*

(*) *if* $K \in S$, $K \notin M(k)$ *and* $\{K\} \cup M(k)$ *is linked then* K *has more than* k *points.*

REMARKS

Ad (b). There is no upperbound, independent of M, to the number of k-point-sets of M_{MIN}. E.g. the 13-mls in P{1,2,...,13} which has the minimal sets {2,3,...,13} and {1,2},{1,3},...,{1,13} has "even 12" two-point-sets.

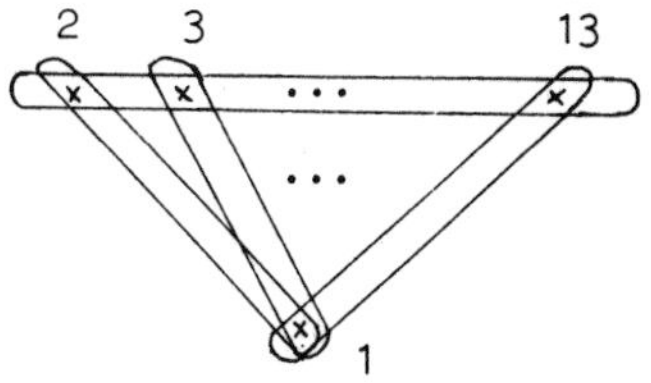

Ad (c). M_{MIN} need not be finite, as was seen in I.2.8.(c).

Before we can proof I.4.1 we first need the following well-known lemma from combinatorial set theory.

I.4.2. LEMMA

For each natural number n each infinite family of sets of at most n points has an infinite quasi-disjoint subfamily.

PROOF

By induction on n.

For n = 1 the family itself is even disjoint, and hence quasidisjoint. Suppose I.4.2 holds for a natural number n, and A is an infinite family of sets of (at most) n+1 points. First choose a maximal disjoint subfamily $A_D \subset A$. If A_D is infinite, then we are ready, so suppose A_D is finite. By its maximality each $A \in \mathcal{A}\backslash\mathcal{A}_D$ meets the finite set $\cup\mathcal{A}_D$. Hence some $a \in \cup\mathcal{A}_D$ must meet infinitely many $A \in \mathcal{A}$. By our induction hypothesis the family

$$\{A\backslash\{a\} \mid a\in A\in\mathcal{A}\}$$

has an infinite quasidisjoint subfamily $\mathcal{A}_Q$. Now

$$\{A\cup\{a\} \mid A\in\mathcal{A}_Q\}$$

is an infinite quasidisjoint subfamily of $\mathcal{A}$.

PROOF OF THEOREM I.4.1.

(a) is trivial because each $S \in \mathcal{M}$ is finite.

(b) Put $\mathcal{M}_k = \{S\in\mathcal{M}_{MIN} \mid S$ has at most k points$\}$ for $k = 1,2,\ldots$. Suppose some $\mathcal{M}_k$ is infinite. By lemma I.4.2 this $\mathcal{M}_k$ has an infinite quasi-disjoint subfamily $\mathcal{M}_Q$, i.e.

$$\exists K \quad \forall S,S' \in \mathcal{M}_Q \quad \text{if } S \neq S' \quad \text{then} \quad S \cap S' = K.$$

Clearly $\exists S \in \mathcal{M}_Q \quad S\backslash K \neq \emptyset$. Choose $p \in S\backslash K$. Because $S \in \mathcal{M}_{MIN}$, we can find a $T \in \mathcal{M}_{MIN}$ such that $S \cap T = \{p\}$ (cf. I.1.10(a)). Consequently $T \cap K = \emptyset$, so T meets $S'\backslash K$ for each $S' \in \mathcal{M}_Q$. Now $\{S'\backslash K \mid S'\in\mathcal{M}_Q\}$ is an infinite disjoint family, contradictory to the finiteness of $T \in \mathcal{S} = P_fX$.

(c) Cf. I.2.3.

(d) The finite families $\mathcal{M}_0,\ldots,\mathcal{M}_k$ and $\mathcal{A}_1,\ldots,\mathcal{A}_k$ are defined inductively as follows:
Let $\mathcal{M}_0$ be the family of all $(\leq k)$-point-sets of $\mathcal{M}_{MIN}$. This family is finite according to (b). If $\mathcal{M}_0,\mathcal{A}_1,\mathcal{M}_1,\ldots,\mathcal{A}_i$ and $\mathcal{M}_i$ are defined for some $i \in \{0,1,\ldots,k-1\}$ then we put

$$\mathcal{A}_{i+1} = \{K\subset\cup\mathcal{M}_i \mid K \text{ has at most } i+1 \text{ points and } \mathcal{M}_i\cup\{K\} \text{ is linked and } K\notin\mathcal{M}_0\}.$$

For each $K \in \mathcal{A}_{i+1}$ we have $K \notin \mathcal{M}$ (otherwise $K \in \mathcal{M}_0$). So we may choose an $M(K) \in \mathcal{M}$ such that

$$K \cap M(K) = \emptyset.$$

Put

$$\mathcal{M}_{i+1} = \mathcal{M}_i \cup \{M(K) \mid K\in\mathcal{A}_{i+1}\}.$$

Finally we take $M(k) = M_k$. Now if $K \in S$, $K \notin M(k)$ and $M(k) \cup \{K\}$ is linked, then $K \notin M_0 \subset M(k)$ and thus $K \notin A_k$. Hence K must have more than k points.

I.5. PRIME SYSTEMS

I.5.1.

Let S be a family of subsets of a set X. In II we will need the following notion:

A subfamily M of S is *prime (in S)* if for any finite number $S_1,\dots,S_n \in S$ with $S_1 \cup \dots S_n = X$ at least one S_i belongs to M.

Some trivial properties of prime systems and their relation to centered systems are mentioned in:

I.5.2. PROPOSITION

(i) *If $M \subset N \subset S$ and M is prime then N is prime.*

(ii) *$M \subset S$ is prime iff $\{X\setminus S \mid S \in S\setminus M\}$ is centered.*

(iii) *$M \subset S$ is a minimal prime system iff $\{X\setminus S \mid S \in S\setminus M\}$ is a maximal centered system.*

(iv) *Each prime system contains a minimal prime system.*

(v) *A minimal prime system is centered.*

(vi) *A maximal centered system is prime.*

We omit the simple proof.

REMARKS

If S satisfies the condition

$$\forall S \in S\ \exists S_1,\dots,S_n \in S \quad X\setminus S = S_1 \cup \dots S_n$$

(e.g. if $S = PX$) then the following converse of (v) and (vi) holds:

(vii) A subsystem of S is minimally prime iff it is maximally centered.

Consider the lattice of all subfamilies of a family S satisfying (vii), ordered by inclusion. There are three types of maximal chains (= by inclusion linearly ordered collections of subfamilies of $\mathcal{S}$):

(i) those chains that contain a minimal prime = maximal centered system. These are the chains which only contain centered systems ("in the lower half") and prime systems ("in the upper half").

(ii) The maximal chains which contain no centered systems, except $\emptyset$ and some {S}, and no prime systems, except $\mathcal{S}$ and some $\mathcal{S}\setminus\{S'\}$.

(iii) The "intermediate" chains which contain some nontrivial centered systems, and some nontrivial linked systems but also a non-centered non-prime family.

Classification of subfamilies in the lattice (PPX,$\subset$) for an infinite set X:

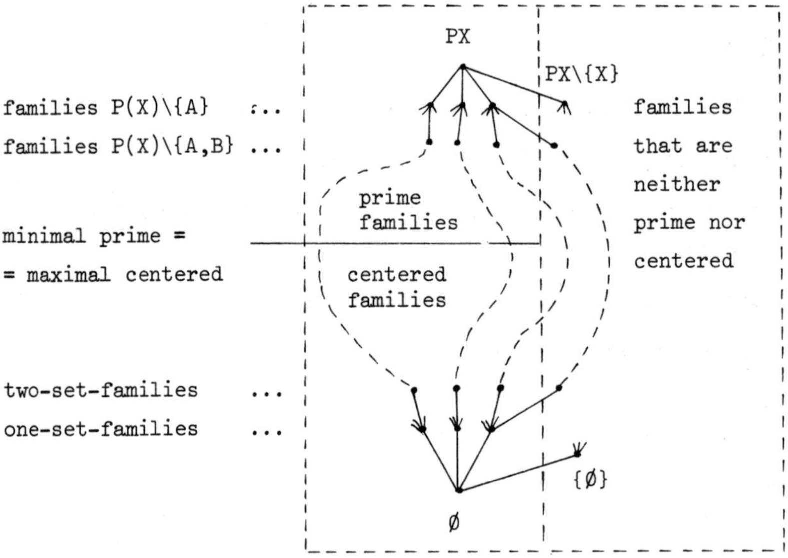

CHAPTER II SUPEREXTENSIONS RELATIVE SUBBASES

Had I the heavens embroidered cloths
Enwrought with golden and silver light
The blue and the dim and the dark cloths
Of the night and the light and the half-light
I would spread the cloths under your feet
But I being poor have only my dreams
Tread softly because you tread on my dreams

(Yeats)

All topological spaces under consideration will be T_1-spaces. For a T_1-space X and a subbase S for the closed sets we will define a T_1-space $\lambda_S(X)$, called the superextension of X with respect to S. The underlying set of $\lambda_S(X)$ will be the family of all mls's in S, i.e. the set-theoretical superextension of S. The topology will be defined in close analogy to the Wallman-type-S-compactification, which has for underlying set all maximal centered systems in S. In order to guarantee that X is (canonically) embedded in $\lambda_S(X)$ (by identification of points in X with fixed mls's), we have to put a mild condition on S, named: S is a T_1-subbase. This condition will be assumed for S throughout this and the next chapters.

After the formal definition of $\lambda_S(X)$ in section 1, section 2 introduces the notion of supercompactness, a property stronger than compactness. The relation between supercompactness and $\lambda_S(X)$ is very similar to the relation between compactness and the Wallman-type-S-extension, $\omega_S(X)$. The major difference is that X is always dense in $\omega_S(X)$, but 'almost never' (cf. II.1.8) in $\lambda_S X$.

The De Groot-Aarts's characterization of complete regularity (cf. [7]) is proved in section 3. This characterization makes essential use of linked systems, in order to abstain from algebraic conditions on the subbase such as being closed under the taking of finite intersections. From this characterization (maximal) linked systems, supercompactness and superextensions originate (cf. II.5.4). Earlier characterizations did involve algebraic conditions on the subbase. The implications of such conditions for $\lambda_S X$ are the subject of section 5. Here also conditions are studied under which two different T_1-subbases S and T for X generate "canonically homeomorphic" superextensions: $\lambda_S X \cong \lambda_T X$. Also the separation axioms and the closure of X in $\lambda_S X$ get attention in the sections 3, 4, 5.

Sufficient conditions for the continuous extension of e.g. the functions $f: X \to \mathbb{R}$ or $g: X \to Y$ to $\bar{f}: \lambda_S X \to \mathbb{R}$ and $\bar{g}: \lambda_S X \to \lambda_T Y$ are given in section 4. This will lead to the result that under suitable conditions the closure of X in $\lambda_S X$ is (homeomorphic to) the Čech-Stone-compactification of X. In general there are no appropriate necessary conditions known.

II.1. DEFINITION AND IMMEDIATE CONSEQUENCES

II.1.1.

Let S be a family of subsets of a set X. Our first concern is to make X into a subset of $\lambda(S)$ by identification of $x \in X$ with $\{S \mid x \in S \in S\}$. So we define:

A family S of subsets of a set X is called a *T_1-family* if $\forall x\ \cap\{S \mid x \in S \in S\} = \{x\}$ and (one of) the following two equivalent conditions hold(s):

(i) $\forall x \in X$ the family $\{S \mid x \in S \in S\}$ is an mls in S.

(ii) $\forall x \in X \forall T \in S \quad x \notin T \Longrightarrow (\exists S \in S \quad x \in S \text{ and } S \cap T = \emptyset)$.

By a *T_1-subbase* for a topological space X we will always mean a T_1-family that is a subbase for the closed sets of X.

II.1.2. REMARKS

Observe that a topological space X has a T_1-subbase iff X is a T_1-space. On the other hand a subbase for the closed sets of a T_1-space need not be a T_1-family; e.g. the family of all cofinite subsets of an infinite set X is a closed subbase for the discrete topology, but this whole family is even linked, contradictory to being a T_1-family.

If S is a T_1-subbase of X, then, not only $\{S \mid x \in S \in S\}$ is an mls for each $x \in X$, but also $\{S \mid x \in S \in S\} \neq \{S \mid y \in S \in S\}$ for different $x, y \in X$. So the map $i: X \to \lambda(S)$ defined by $i(x) = \{S \mid x \in S \in S\}$ maps X 1-1, onto the fixed mls's in $\lambda(S)$.

If $S \subset P(X)$ is arbitrary, then $S^* = S \cup \{\{x\} \mid x \in X\}$ is a T_1-subbase (viz. for the smallest T_1-topology in which S is a family of closed sets). Moreover $\lambda(S)$ and $\lambda(S^*)$ contain precisely the same free mls's. So the following restriction involves no essential loss of generality.

FROM NOW ON IN CHAPTER II-V, WE RESTRICT OURSELVES TO T_1-SPACES WITH T_1-SUBBASES. IN PARTICULAR

X *WILL ALWAYS BE A* T_1*-SPACE, AND*
$\mathcal{S}$ *WILL ALWAYS BE A* T_1*-SUBBASE FOR* X.
$\mathcal{G}$ *IS THE FAMILY OF ALL CLOSED SUBSETS OF* X.
$\mathcal{O}$ *IS THE FAMILY OF ALL OPEN SUBSETS OF* X.
$\mathcal{Z}$ *IS THE FAMILY OF ALL ZEROSETS OF* X.

THE FUNCTION $i: X \to \lambda_{\mathcal{S}}X$ *IS DEFINED BY*

$$i(x) = \{S \mid x \in S \in \mathcal{S}\}.$$

FOR ANY FAMILY A *WE DEFINE*

$A^{\cap}$ = *the family of intersections of subfamilies of* A.

$A^{\cup}$ = *the family of unions of subfamilies of* A.

$A^{\textcircled{f}\cap}$ = *the family of intersections of finite subfamilies of* A.

$A^{\textcircled{f}\cup}$ = *the family of unions of finite subfamilies of* A.

II.1.3.

Before we introduce a topology on $\lambda(\mathcal{S})$, we need the following definition, in analogy to the Wallman-type-compactification.

For each $S \in \mathcal{S}$ we define

$$S^{+} = \{M \mid S \in M \in \lambda(\mathcal{S})\}.$$

It is useful to generalize the operator to arbitrary subsets $A \subset X$ in the following way:

$$A^{+} = \{M \mid M \in \lambda(\mathcal{S}) \text{ and } \exists S \in M \quad S \subset A\}.$$

Some properties of this operation are given in the following proposition, the simple proof of which is omitted.

II.1.4. PROPOSITION

(i) *If* $A \subset B \subset X$ *then* $A^{+} \subset B^{+}$

(ii) *If* $A, B \subset X$ *and* $A \cap B = \emptyset$ *then* $A^+ \cap B^+ = \emptyset$

(iii) *If* $S, T \in \mathcal{S}$ *then* $S \cap T = \emptyset$ *iff* $S^+ \cap T^+ = \emptyset$

(iv) *If* $S, T \in \mathcal{S}$ *then* $S \cup T = X$ *iff* $S^+ \cup T^+ = \lambda(\mathcal{S})$

(v) *If* $S \in \mathcal{S}$ *then* $S^+ \cup (X \backslash S)^+ = \lambda(\mathcal{S})$

(*and by* (ii): $S^+ \cap (X \backslash S)^+ = \emptyset$)

(vi) $\forall S \in \mathcal{S} \qquad i^{-1}(S^+) = S$

(vii) *If* $M \in \lambda(\mathcal{S})$ *and* $\mathcal{A} \subset \mathcal{S}$ *then* $\mathcal{A} \subset M$ *iff* $M \in \cap\{A^+ \mid A \in \mathcal{A}\}$

II.1.5.

Now $\mathcal{S}^+ = \{S^+ \mid S \in \mathcal{S}\}$ is taken as subbase for the closed sets of a topology on $\lambda(\mathcal{S})$. The resulting topological space is called the *superextension of* $(X, \mathcal{S})$ or the *superextension of* X *with respect to* or *relative* $\mathcal{S}$. It is denoted by

$$\lambda_{\mathcal{S}}(X) \quad \text{or} \quad \lambda_{\mathcal{S}}X.$$

THE superextension of X is the superextension of X with respect to the closed subbase consisting of all closed sets, and will be denoted by

$$\lambda(X) \quad \text{or} \quad \lambda X, \quad (\text{or } \lambda_{\mathcal{G}}X \text{ or } \lambda_{\mathcal{G}}(X)).$$

X is in general not dense in $\lambda_{\mathcal{S}}(X)$, see II.1.8. The closure of X in $\lambda_{\mathcal{S}}(X)$ will be denoted by

$$\beta_{\mathcal{S}}(X) = X^- \subset \lambda_{\mathcal{S}}(X).$$

This notation was originally chosen because if $\mathcal{S}$ is the family of all closed sets in a normal space, or the family of all zerosets in a Tychonoff-space, then $\beta_{\mathcal{S}}(X)$ is homeomorphic to $\beta(X)$, the Čech-Stone-compactification of X (see II.4.4).

We proceed with some immediate consequences. The first is a trivial corollary of II.1.4.(v).

II.1.6. PROPOSITION

The family $\{(X \backslash S)^+ \mid S \in \mathcal{S}\}$ *is an open subbase for* $\lambda_{\mathcal{S}}(X)$.

II.1.7. PROPOSITION

(a) $\beta_S(X) = \cap\{S_1^+ \cup \ldots S_n^+ \mid S_i \in S$ *and* $S_1 \cup \ldots S_n = X, n \in \mathbb{N}\}$

(b) *For* $M \in \lambda_S(X)$ *the following conditions are equivalent:*

(i) $M \in \beta_S(X)$.

(ii) M *is prime (i.e. from each finite cover of* X *by elements of* S*, at least one element belongs to* M*, cf. I.5).*

(iii) M *contains a prime centered system.*

PROOF

(a) Note that the sets $S_1^+ \cup \ldots S_n^+$ for $S_1,\ldots,S_n \in S$ form a base for the closed sets in $\lambda_S(X)$.

(b) (i) $\Longleftrightarrow$ (ii) follows from (a) and (ii) $\Longrightarrow$ (iii) follows from I.5.2.(iv) and (v). Finally (iii) $\Longrightarrow$ (ii) is trivial (cf. I.5.2.(i)).

That "almost always" $\beta_S X \neq \lambda_S X$ can be seen from

II.1.8. PROPOSITION

If X *is Hausdorff and has at least 3 points, then* X *is not dense in* λX*. In fact any free fmls in* G *does not belong to the closure,* $\beta_G(X)$*, of* X *in* λX.

PROOF

If p, q and r $\in$ X then $\{\{p,q\},\{q,r\},\{r,p\}\}$ is a pre-mls for a free fmls in λX. Next let M be an arbitrary free fmls, defined on the finite set M. Because X is Hausdorff we can find pairwise disjoint neighbourhoods U_p, $p \in M$. Because M is free, each $S \in M$ contains at least two points of M, i.e. $M \notin (U_p^-)^+$ for each $p \in M$. Also $M \notin (X \setminus \cup\{U_p \mid p \in M\})^+$. However $\{U_p^- \mid p \in M\} \cup \{X \setminus \cup\{U_p \mid p \in M\}\}$ is a finite cover of X by closed sets. So by II.1.7.a $M \notin \beta_G X$.

II.2. COMPACTNESS AND SUPERCOMPACTNESS

II.2.1.

By Alexanders lemma a topological space is compact iff it has a closed subbase such that each (maximal) centered system of subbase elements has a non-empty intersection. We define:

A topological space is *supercompact* if it has a binary, closed subbase. Here, a family of sets is called *binary* if each (maximal) linked subsystem has a non-empty intersection.

II.2.2. REMARKS

(1) Each supercompact space clearly is compact.

(2) The canonical subbase of right- and left-tails of a linearly ordered compact space is binary.

(3) The canonical subbase of a product of supercompact spaces is binary, so supercompactness is a product invariant. As a consequence of 2 all topological (hyper) cubes (= all products of closed intervals) are supercompact.

(4) The topological sum of finitely many supercompact spaces is supercompact.

(5) X is supercompact iff for some (T_1-) subbase T $\lambda_T X = i(X)$ holds.

(6) If a closed base of a T_1-space is binary, then this space contains at most two points.

(7) If S is binary and $S^{\cap}$ denotes the family of all intersections of arbitrary subfamilies of S, then also $S^{\cap}$ is binary.

(8) There exists a compact T_1-space X with the following properties:

  (i) X is not supercompact,

  (ii) X can be written as a union of two supercompact T_1-spaces or of three supercompact metric spaces,

  (iii) X is the quotient of a supercompact metric space under a quotientmap with finite point-inverses.

  (iv) X can be made supercompact by adjunction of one point.

(9) J.L. O'Connor [15] has proved that every compact metrizable space is supercompact. We do not know whether every compact Hausdorff space and in particular whether $\beta\mathbb{N}$ is supercompact or not.

Proof of 8. Let $\{p,q,r\}$ be a three-point-set and put

$$P = \mathbb{N} \times \{p\}$$
$$Q = \mathbb{N} \times \{q\}$$
$$R = \mathbb{N} \times \{r\}$$
$$X = \mathbb{N} \times \{p,q,r\} \cup \{p,q,r\}$$

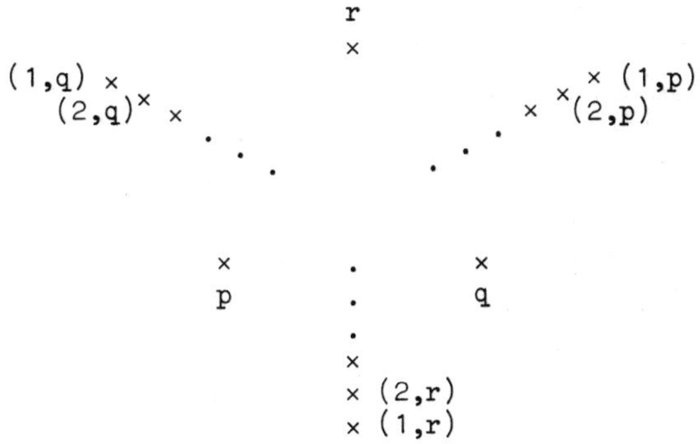

We define a topology on X by making $P \cup Q \cup R$ into isolated points, and making P converge to $\{q,r\}$, Q to $\{r,p\}$ and R to $\{p,q\}$:

$$O \subset X \text{ is open iff } \begin{cases} p \in O \Longrightarrow (Q \cup R)\backslash O \text{ is finite} \\ q \in O \Longrightarrow (R \cup P)\backslash O \text{ is finite} \\ r \in O \Longrightarrow (P \cup Q)\backslash O \text{ is finite} \end{cases}$$

Proof of 8 (ii).

$$X = (P\cup\{q,r\}) \cup (Q\cup R\cup\{p\}) = (P\cup\{q\}) \cup (Q\cup\{r\}) \cup (R\cup\{p\}).$$

Now $Q \cup R \cup \{p\}$, $Q \cup \{p\}$, $Q \cup \{r\}$, $R \cup \{p\}$ and the subset of the real line $\{0\} \cup \{\frac{1}{n} \mid n=1,2,\ldots\}$ are homeomorphic, and the last space is a compact linearly ordered topological space, and hence supercompact (remark 2). So we only have to produce a binary closed subbase for $P \cup \{q,r\}$. As such we can take e.g.

$$\{\{x\} \mid x\in P\cup\{q,r\}\} \cup \{P\cup\{q,r\}\backslash\{x\} \mid x\in P\}$$

Proof of 8 (iii). Let Y be the following subset of the place

$$Y = (\{0\} \cup \{\tfrac{1}{n} \mid n\in\mathbb{N}\}) \times \{1,2,3,4,5,6\}.$$

Identify in Y $(\frac{1}{n},k)$ with $(\frac{1}{n},l)$ if $k = l \bmod 3$, and $(0,k)$ with $(0,l)$ if $\{k,l\}$ is one of the pairs $\{1,2\}$, $\{3,4\}$ or $\{5,6\}$. The thus obtained quotient space is homeomorfic to X. Moreover Y is supercompact by (2) and and (3): a binary subbase for Y is e.g.:

$$\{\{y\} \mid y\in Y\} \cup \{Y\backslash\{(\tfrac{1}{n},k)\} \mid (\tfrac{1}{n},k)\in Y\}.$$

Proof of 8 (i). Suppose S is a subbase for the closed sets of X. Consider the closed set $P \cup \{q,r\}$ and $x \in X \setminus (P \cup \{q,r\})$. We can find finitely many subbase elements, covering $P \cup \{q,r\}$, none of which contains x. So far one of these subbase elements, denoted by $S(P,-x)$, we must have:

$$S(P,-x) \cap P \text{ is infinite, so } q,r \in S(P,-x)$$

and

$$x \notin S(P,-x) \in S.$$

Look at $S(P,-p)$. Because $p \notin S(P,-p)$, $S(P,-p)$ meets $R \cup Q$ in only finitely many points, say $x_1,\ldots,x_n$. Then $\{q,r\} \subset S(P,-p) \cap S(P,-x_1) \cap \ldots$ $\ldots S(P,-x_n) \subset P \cup \{q,r\}$. Similarly we can find $S(Q,q),S(Q,-y_1),\ldots,S(R,-z_l)$ such that

$$\{r,p\} \subset S(Q,-q) \cap S(Q,-y_1) \cap \ldots S(Q,-y_m) \subset Q \cup \{r,p\}$$

$$\{p,q\} \subset S(R,-r) \cap S(R,-z_1) \cap \ldots S(R,-z_l) \subset R \cup \{p,q\}.$$

Now

$$\{S(P,-p),S(Q,-q),S(R,-r),S(P,-x_i),S(Q,-y_j),S(R,-z_k) \mid i,j,k\}$$

is a free linked system. So S can never be binary.

Proof of 8 (iv). Put $Y = X \cup \{s\}$, where X is open in Y, and s has for neighbourhood only all cofinite subsets (i.e. sets with a finite complement) of Y that contain s. A binary subbasis for Y consists of all singletons of Y and all cofinite subsets of $P \cup \{q,r,s\}$, $Q \cup \{r,p,s\}$ and $R \cup \{p,q,s\}$.

II.2.3. THEOREM

Every superextension $\lambda_S X$ is (super-) compact. In fact the subbase S^+ is binary.

REMARK

The proof of the supercompactness of $\lambda_S X$ is quite similar to the proof of the compactness of the Wallman-type-compactification of X.

PROOF

Let $\{S_\alpha^+ \mid \alpha \in J\}$ be a linked subfamily of $\{S^+ \mid S \in \mathcal{S}\}$. By II.1.4.iii $\{S_\alpha \mid \alpha \in J\}$ is a linked subfamily of $\mathcal{S}$. Let M be any mls in $\mathcal{S}$, containing this family. Then $M \in \cap\{S_\alpha^+ \mid \alpha \in J\}$ (cf. II.1.4.vii).

COROLLARY

The closure of X *in the superextension,* $\beta_{\mathcal{S}}X$, *is a compactification of* X.

II.3. A TOPOLOGICAL CHARACTERIZATION OF COMPLETE REGULARITY

II.3.1.

The characterization mentioned in the title is due to De Groot and Aarts, [7], and appears here as theorem II.3.5. This and several other known and new characterizations are discussed and generalized by P. Hamburger, see [10].

First we need some definitions. Normality is usually defined as a property of topologies (i.e. very special families of sets), using both open and closed sets. *) Here we define normality in terms of closed sets only and moreover we generalize the definition, so that it becomes applicable to (closed) subbases, i.e. arbitrary families of sets.

An arbitrary family $\mathcal{A}$ of subsets of A is *normal* if for any two disjoint $A_1, A_2 \in \mathcal{A}$ there exist $A_1', A_2' \in \mathcal{A}$ such that

---

*)

"This nomenclature is an excellent example of the time-honored custom of referring to a problem we cannot handle as abnormal, irregular, improper, degenerate, inadmissible, or otherwise undesirable", J.L. Kelly - General Topology, p. 112.

"What we call "normal" is a product of repression, denial, splitting, projection and introjection and other forms of destructive action on experience. It is radically estranged from the structure of being ... Society highly values its normal man. It educates children to lose themselves and to become absurd and thus to be normal", R.D. Laing - The Politics of Experience.

$A_1 \cap A_1' = \emptyset$

$A_2 \cap A_2' = \emptyset$

$A_1' \cup A_2' = A.$

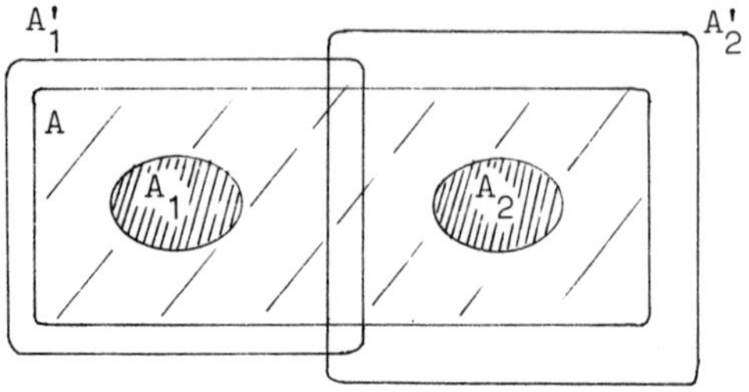

$(A_2 \backslash A = A_1 \backslash A = \emptyset\ !)$

An arbitrary family $\mathcal{A}$ of subsets of A is *weakly normal* if for any disjoint $A_1, A_2 \in \mathcal{A}$ there exist finitely many $B_1, \ldots, B_n \in \mathcal{A}$ such that each B_i meets at most one of A_1, A_2 and $\cup B_i = A$.

REMARKS

(i) Any normal family is weakly normal.

(ii) The collection of all closed sets, $\mathcal{G}$, of a T_1-space X is (weakly) normal iff X is normal.

(iii) The zerosets, $\mathcal{Z}$, of a Tychonoff-space X constitute a normal T_1-subbase.

(iv) A weakly normal family that is closed under the taking of finite unions, is normal.

II.3.2. THEOREM

If $\mathcal{S}$ is a normal T_1-subbase for X, then $\lambda_{\mathcal{S}}X$ is T_2.

PROOF

Let $\mathcal{M}$, $\mathcal{N}$ be two different mls's in $\mathcal{S}$. By I.1.4.c there exist disjoint $S, T \in \mathcal{S}$ with $S \in \mathcal{M}$, $T \in \mathcal{N}$. Since $\mathcal{S}$ is normal there exist $S_0, T_0 \in \mathcal{S}$ with

(i) $\quad S \cap S_0 = \emptyset$

(ii) $\quad T \cap T_0 = \emptyset$

(iii) $\quad S_0 \cup T_0 = X$

By (iii) and II.1.4.iv $S_0^+ \cup T_0^+ = \lambda_{\mathcal{S}}X$. Hence $\lambda_{\mathcal{S}}X \backslash S_0^+$ and $\lambda_{\mathcal{S}}X \backslash T_0^+$ are disjoint open neighbourhoods of $\mathcal{M}$ and $\mathcal{N}$ respectively.

II.3.3. THEOREM

If S is a weakly normal T_1-subbase then $\beta_S X$ is T_2.

PROOF

Let M, N be two different mls's in $\beta_S X$, and $S \in M$, $T \in N$ disjoint. Because S is weakly normal, there exists a finite cover of X by elements $H_1,\ldots,H_n$ of S, each of which meets at most one of S and T, say $(H_1 \cup \ldots H_k) \cap S = \emptyset$ and $(H_{k+1} \cup \ldots H_n) \cap T = \emptyset$. It follows that $(H_1^+ \cup \ldots H_n^+) \supset$ $\supset X$ and hence $H_1^+ \cup \ldots H_n^+ \supset X^- = \beta_S X$ (cf. II.1.7). So $\beta_S X \backslash (H_1^+ \cup \ldots H_k^+)$ and $\beta_S X \backslash (H_{k+1}^+ \ldots H_n^+)$ are disjoint open neighbourhoods of M and N in $\beta_S X$.

II.3.4. THEOREM

Let X *be a T_1-space* X *and* G *the family of all closed sets. Then the following properties are equivalent:*

(i) X is normal,

(ii) $\lambda X = \lambda_G X$ is normal (compact + T_2),

(iii) $\beta_G X$ is normal (compact + T_2),

(iv) $\beta_G X \cong \beta X$, the Čech-Stone compactification.

PROOF

(i) $\Longrightarrow$ (ii) is II.3.2; (ii) $\Longrightarrow$ (iii) is trivial; (iii) $\Longrightarrow$ (i): Suppose S and T are disjoint closed sets in X, and $\beta_G X$ is normal. Then $S^+ \cap \beta_G X$ and $T^+ \cap \beta_G X$ are disjoint closed subsets of $\beta_G X$ (cf. II.1.4.iii) which thus have disjoint open neighbourhoods, say U and V, in $\beta_G X$. Then $i^{-1}U$ and $i^{-1}V$ are disjoint open neighbourhoods of S and T.
(i) $\Longrightarrow$ (iv) will be a corollary to II.4.3 and (iv) $\Longrightarrow$ (iii) is trivial again.

II.3.5.

It follows from remarks (i) and (iii) above and II.3.3 that the following conditions on a T_1-space X are equivalent.

(i) X has a T_2-compactification (i.e. X is $T_{3\frac{1}{2}}$),

(ii) There is a closed, normal T_1-subbase for X.

(iii) There is a closed, weakly normal T_1-subbase for X.

We state this as a theorem (cf. II.5.4).

THEOREM [De Groot-Aarts]

A T_1-space X is completely regular iff X has a (weakly) normal, closed T_1-subbase.

II.4. EXTENSION OF FUNCTIONS

Two types of extensions will be considered:

$$\begin{array}{ccc} X & \xrightarrow{f} & \mathbb{R} \\ \downarrow & \nearrow & \\ \lambda_S(X) & & \exists \bar{f}? \end{array} \qquad \text{and} \qquad \begin{array}{ccc} X & \xrightarrow{f} & Y \\ \downarrow & \exists \bar{f}? & \downarrow \\ \lambda_S X & \dashrightarrow & \lambda_T Y \end{array}$$

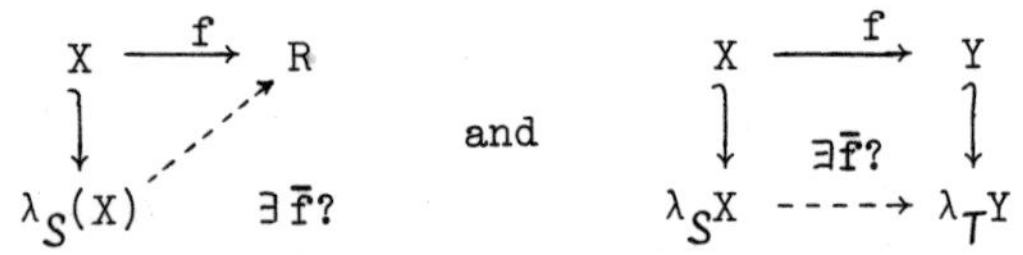

II.4.1. THEOREM

If S is a T_1-subbase for a T_1-space X, and S contains all zerosets, then each continuous, bounded real-valued function $f: X \to \mathbb{R}$ has a continuous, bounded extension $\bar{f}: \lambda_S X \to \mathbb{R}$ defined by

$$\forall M \in \lambda_S X \qquad \bar{f}(M) = \inf_{S \in M} \sup f(S).$$

PROOF

Put $\mathbb{R}^+ = \{x \in \mathbb{R} \mid x > 0\}$. We will show that

(i) $\forall a \in \mathbb{R}\ [\bar{f}^{-1}(-\infty,a]$ is closed]

(ii) $\forall a \in \mathbb{R}\ [\bar{f}^{-1}[a,\infty)$ is closed]

(i): $M \in \bar{f}^{-1}(-\infty,a]$

$\iff \inf_{S \in M} \sup f(S) \leq a$

$\iff \forall \varepsilon \in \mathbb{R}^+ \exists S \in M f(S) \subseteq (-\infty,a+\varepsilon]$

$\iff \forall \varepsilon \in \mathbb{R}^+ f^{-1}(-\infty,a+\varepsilon] \in M$

$\iff M \in \bigcap_{\varepsilon \in \mathbb{R}^+} (f^{-1}(-\infty,a+\varepsilon])^+$

(ii): $\mathcal{M} \in \bar{f}^{-1}[a,\infty)$

$$\iff \inf_{S\in\mathcal{M}} \sup f(S) \geq a$$

$$\iff \forall S \in \mathcal{M} \sup f(S) \geq a$$

$$\iff \forall S \in \mathcal{M} \forall \varepsilon \in \mathbb{R}^+ S \cap f^{-1}[a-\varepsilon,\infty) \neq \emptyset$$

$$\iff \forall \varepsilon \in \mathbb{R}^+ f^{-1}[a-\varepsilon,\infty) \in \mathcal{M}$$

$$\iff \mathcal{M} \in \bigcap_{\varepsilon\in\mathbb{R}^+} (f^{-1}[a-\varepsilon,\infty))^+$$

II.4.2.

Note that of course the above extension $\bar{f}$ is, in general, not unique, if X is not dense in $\lambda_S X$. Let F be the following family of (bounded) continuous functions

$$F = \{g: \lambda_S(X)\to\mathbb{R} \mid g^{-1}(0)\supset X\}.$$

Then $\{\bar{f}+g \mid g\in F\}$ is the collection of possible extensions of $\bar{f}$.

As an immediate corollary of II.4.1 and II.3.3 and the fact that the zerosets, Z, of a Tychonoff space are a normal T_1-base we obtain:

II.4.3. THEOREM

If X *is a* T_1*-space and* S *a (weakly) normal* T_1*-subbase, which contains all zerosets of* X*, then* X *is completely regular, and the closure of* X *in* $\lambda_S X$ *is the Cech-Stone-compactification of* X*:*

$$\beta_S(X) = \beta(X).$$

REMARK

Note that the condition of S being weakly normal is essential. E.g. if $S = G$ is the family of all closed sets and X is completely regular but not normal, then $\beta_S(X)$ is not Hausdorff (cf. II.3.4 and II.3.1.(ii)).

II.4.4. COROLLARY

(i) *If* X *is Tychonoff and* $\mathcal{Z}$ *the family of all zerosets in* X, *then*

$$\beta_{\mathcal{Z}}(X) = \beta(X).$$

(ii) *If* $\mathcal{G}$ *is the family of all closed sets in a* T_1*-space* X, *then*

$$\beta_{\mathcal{G}}(X) = \beta(X)$$

iff X *is normal.*

The other type of extension is covered by

II.4.5. THEOREM G.A. Jensen [9], thm. 2.1.

Let $\mathcal{S}$ *be a* T_1*-subbase for* X, *let* $\mathcal{T}$ *be a normal* T_1*-subbase for* Y *and let* f *be a continuous map* f: X → Y *such that*

$$\forall T \in \mathcal{T} \quad f^{-1}T \in \mathcal{S}.$$

Then

$$\forall M \in \lambda_{\mathcal{S}}X \quad \{T \in \mathcal{T} \mid f^{-1}T \in M\}$$

is a pre-mls in $\mathcal{T}$, *and the function*

$$\bar{f}: \lambda_{\mathcal{S}}(X) \to \lambda_{\mathcal{T}}(Y)$$

defined by

$$\bar{f}(M) = \underline{\{T \in \mathcal{T} \mid f^{-1}T \in M\}}$$

is a continuous closed extension of f.
Moreover, if f *is onto, then* $\bar{f}$ *is onto.*
If f *is* 1-1 *and* $\forall S \in \mathcal{S}$ $f(S) \in \mathcal{T}$ *then* $\bar{f}$ *is an embedding.*

PROOF

Clearly $\{T \in \mathcal{T} \mid f^{-1}T \in M\}$ is linked. Suppose $T_i \in \mathcal{T}$, i = 1,2, both meet all T from this family, but $T_1 \cap T_2 = \emptyset$. By the normality of $\mathcal{T}$ there exists $T_i' \in \mathcal{T}$, i = 1,2, such that

$$T_i \cap T_i' = \emptyset, \quad i = 1,2,$$

and

$$T_1' \cup T_2' = Y.$$

Hence $f^{-1}T_1' \cup f^{-1}T_2' = X$ and (by I.1.11.b) $f^{-1}(T_i') \in \mathcal{M}$ for at least one i. Suppose $f^{-1}T_1' \in \mathcal{M}$. Then $T_1 \cap T_1' = \emptyset$ provides a contradiction to our assumptions on T_1. So (by I.1.9.a) $\{T \in \mathcal{T} \mid f^{-1}T \in \mathcal{M}\}$ is a pre-mls.

For the continuity of $\bar{f}$, we only have to show for all $T_0 \in \mathcal{T}$ that $\bar{f}^{-1}(T_0^+)$ is closed in $\lambda_{\mathcal{S}}X$. Suppose $\mathcal{M} \in \lambda_{\mathcal{S}}X \backslash \bar{f}^{-1}(T_0^+)$. I.e. $\bar{f}(\mathcal{M}) \cup \{T_0\}$ or equivalently

$$\{T \in \mathcal{T} \mid f^{-1}T \in \mathcal{M}\} \cup \{T_0\}$$

is not linked.

Hence $\exists T_1 \in \mathcal{T} \quad f^{-1}T_1 \in \mathcal{M}$ and $T_1 \cap T_0 = \emptyset$. Choose $T_i' \in \mathcal{T}$ such that $T_i \cap T_i' = \emptyset$, $i = 1,2$, and $T_0' \cup T_1' = Y$. Then $f^{-1}T_0' \cup f^{-1}T_1' = X$, so $(f^{-1}T_0')^+ \cup (f^{-1}T_1')^+ = \lambda_{\mathcal{S}}X$. Moreover $(f^{-1}T_0')^+ \cap \bar{f}^{-1}(T_0^+) = \emptyset$ and $(f^{-1}T_1') \notin \mathcal{M}$, so

$$\mathcal{M} \in \lambda_{\mathcal{S}}X \backslash (f^{-1}T_1')^+ \subset \lambda_{\mathcal{S}}X \backslash \bar{f}^{-1}(T_0^+).$$

Hence $\lambda_{\mathcal{S}}X \backslash (f^{-1}T_1')^+$ is a (subbasic) open neighbourhood of $\mathcal{M}$, which is disjoint of $\bar{f}^{-1}(T_0^+)$.

Because $\mathcal{T}$ is normal, $\lambda_{\mathcal{T}}Y$ is Hausdorff (II.3.2). Now $\bar{f}: \lambda_{\mathcal{S}}X \to \lambda_{\mathcal{T}}Y$ is a continuous map from a compact space onto a Hausdorff space, so $\bar{f}$ is a closed map.

Next we show that

$$\begin{array}{ccc} X & \xrightarrow{\quad f \quad} & Y \\ \Big\downarrow i_x & \star & \Big\downarrow i_y \\ \lambda_{\mathcal{S}}(X) & \xrightarrow{\quad \bar{f} \quad} & \lambda_{\mathcal{S}}(Y) \end{array}$$

commutes, i.e. $\bar{f}$ is an extension of f. Let $x \in X$ and $y = f(x)$. Then

$$\{S \mid x \in S \in \mathcal{S}\} \supset \{f^{-1}T \mid y \in T \in \mathcal{T}\}.$$

Hence $\bar{f}i_x(x) = \bar{f}\{S \mid x \in S \in \mathcal{S}\} = \{T \mid y \in T \in \mathcal{T}\} = i_y(y) = i_y f(x)$.

If f is onto and $\mathcal{M} \in \lambda_{\mathcal{T}}(Y)$, then $\{f^{-1}T \mid T \in \mathcal{M}\}$ is a linked subfamily of $\mathcal{S}$. Any mls in $\mathcal{S}$, which contains this family is clearly mapped by $\bar{f}$ onto $\mathcal{M}$. Hence $\bar{f}$ is also onto.

Finally suppose f is 1-1 and $\forall S \in \mathcal{S} \quad f(S) \in \mathcal{T}$. Then $\bar{f}$ is 1-1. For suppose $M,N \in \lambda(S)$, $M \neq N$, $S \in M$, $S' \in N$ and $S \cap S' = \emptyset$. Then $fS \cap fS' = \emptyset$ and $fS, fS' \in T$. So $\bar{f}(S) \in \bar{f}M \setminus \bar{f}N$, i.e. $\bar{f}M \neq \bar{f}N$.

COROLLARY 1

If T is a normal T_1-subbase of a T_1-space X then $\lambda_T X$ is a Hausdorff quotient of λX, under a continuous map, that is identity on X.

REMARKS

Corollary 1 will be used in III.4.1.CORO to prove local connectedness for $\lambda_T X$ if X is connected and T is a normal T_1-subbase. There we first prove that λX is locally connected, and then apply corollary 1. Because of the self-chosen-restrictions on the definition of an fmls, there do not always exist fmls's in T, and we are not able to give a more direct proof.

In V one finds examples of subbases S for $[0,1]$ such that $\lambda_S[0,1]$ is not connected, or connected but not locally connected. This shows that $\lambda_S X$ is not always a continuous image of λX, so the condition of normality of S cannot be neglected. Yet it is well possible, that it can be weakened considerably.

COROLLARY 2. SUPEREXTENSIONS OF SUBSPACES

If X is a subspace of Y, S is a T_1-subbase for X and T is a T_1-subbase for Y, then $\lambda_S X$ is naturally embedded in $\lambda_T Y$ in each of the following cases:

(a) *X is closed in Y,*
Y is normal and
S and T consist of all closed sets of X resp. Y.

(b) *X is a zeroset in Y,*
Y is Tychonoff and
S and T consist of all zerosets in X resp. Y.

(c) *(most general corollary of the thm:)*
$S = \{T \cap X \mid T \in T\} \subset T$

COROLLARY 3. SUPEREXTENSIONS OF PRODUCTS

If S_i *is a* T_1*-subbase for* X_i, $i \in J$ *and* $S = \bigcup_{i\in J} \{\pi_i^{-1}S \mid S\in S_i\}$ *is the corresponding subbases for* $\Pi\{X_i \mid i\in J\}$ *then* S *is a* T_1*-family and the canonical map*

$$h: \lambda_S\Pi\{X_i \mid i\in J\} \longrightarrow \Pi\{\lambda_{S_i}X_i \mid i\in J\}$$

defined by

$$M \longmapsto (M_i)_{i\in J}$$

where

$$M_i = \underline{\{S\in S_i \mid \pi_i^{-1}S\in M\}}$$

is a homeomorphism. If moreover the S_i *are normal for all* $i \in J$ *then the map*

$$g: \lambda\Pi\{X_i \mid i\in J\} \to \Pi\{\lambda_{S_i}X_i \mid i\in J\}$$

defined by

$$M \longmapsto (M_i)_{i\in J}$$

where again

$$M_i = \underline{\{S\in S_i \mid \pi_i^{-1}S\in M\}}$$

is a continuous, closed, surjective extension of "$\mathrm{id}_{\Pi X_i}$". *Of course,* g *is, in general, not* 1-1.

PROOF

The remarks on h are trivial. For g, apply the theorem to each projectionmap

$$\pi_i: \Pi\{X_i \mid i\in J\} \to X_i.$$

This gives extensions $\bar{\pi}_i: \lambda\Pi\{X_i \mid i\in J\} \to \lambda_{S_i}X_i$, that can be composed to a $g: \lambda\Pi\{X_i \mid i\in J\} \to \Pi\{\lambda_{S_i}X_i \mid i\in J\}$. If $J = \{0,1\}$ and $X_{1,2}$ are two-point-spaces, S_i = all closed sets, then $\lambda_{S_i}X_i \cong X_i$ and $\Pi\{\lambda_{S_i}X_i \mid i\in\{0,1\}\}$ is a four-point-space. However $X_1 \times X_2$ is also a four-point-space and $\lambda(X_1\times X_2)$ is a twelve-point-space. This shows that g is in general not 1-1.

COROLLARY 4. ON RETRACTS

If r: X → Y *is a retraction,* S *and* T *are normal* T_1*-subbases for* X *and* Y *such that*

$$\forall T \in T \quad r^{-1}T \in S \quad \text{and} \quad T \in S$$

and

$$\forall S \in S \quad S \cap Y \in T \subset S$$

then $\bar{r}: \lambda_S(X) \to \lambda_T(Y)$ *is (homeomorphic to) a retraction.*

COROLLARY 5

Let

$\underline{T_4}$ = *the category of* T_4*-spaces and continuous maps*

$\underline{T_{3\frac{1}{2}}}$ = *the category of* $T_{3\frac{1}{2}}$*-spaces and continuous maps*

$\underline{CT_2}$ = *the category of compact* T_2*-spaces and continuous maps.*

Then $\lambda = \lambda_G$ *and* λ_Z *induce covariant functors* $\underline{T_4} \to \underline{CT_2}$ *and* $\underline{T_{3\frac{1}{2}}} \to \underline{CT_2}$.

Analogous to II.4.5 we have theorem II.4.6 for extensions

$$\begin{array}{ccc} X & \xrightarrow{\quad f \quad} & Y \\ {\scriptstyle i}\downarrow & & \downarrow{\scriptstyle i} \\ \beta_S X & \overset{\exists \bar{f}?}{\dashrightarrow} & \beta_T Y \end{array}$$

Now the condition of normality is replaced by weak normality.

II.4.6. THEOREM

Let S *be a* T_1*-subbase for* X, *and* T *a weakly normal* T_1*-subbase for* Y, *and let* f *be a continuous function of* X *into* Y *such that*

$$\forall T \in T \quad f^{-1}T \in S.$$

Then $\forall M \in \beta_S(X) \quad \{T \in T \mid f^{-1}T \in M\}$ *is a pre-mls in* $\lambda(T)$ *and the function*

$$\bar{f}: \beta_S X \to \beta_T Y$$

$$\bar{f}(M) = \underline{\{T \in T \mid f^{-1}T \in M\}}$$

is a continuous extension of f.
Moreoever if f *is onto then* $\bar{f}$ *is onto. If* f *is* 1-1 *and* $\forall S \in \mathcal{S}$ $f(S) \in \mathcal{T}$, *then* $\bar{f}$ *is an embedding.*

COROLLARY

If $\mathcal{T}$ *is a weakly normal* T_1*-subbase of the* T_1*-space* X *then* $\beta_{\mathcal{T}}X$ *is a Hausdorff quotient of* $\beta_G X$.

PROOF

The proof is almost literary the same as the proof of II.4.5, except for some replacements of λ by β, and of two-element covers by finite covers.

II.4.7.

Although the extension $\bar{f}$ of f in II.4.5 is not a unique extension of f, it depends continuously on f, at least if X is compact, in the following sense. (Here I = [0,1] is the closed interval of real numbers.)

THEOREM

Let $\mathcal{S}$ *be a* T_1*-subbase for the compact* T_1*-space* X, *and* $\mathcal{T}$ *a normal* T_1*-subbase for* Y. *Then a homotopy* $H: X \times I \to Y$ *which satisfies* $H_t^{-1}T \in \mathcal{S}$ *for all* $t \in I$ *and* $T \in \mathcal{T}$ *has a continuous extension*

$$\begin{array}{ccc} X\times I & \xrightarrow{\;H\;} & Y \\ \downarrow{\scriptstyle i_X\times id} & & \downarrow{\scriptstyle i_Y} \\ \lambda_{\mathcal{S}}X\times I & \xrightarrow{\;\bar{H}\;} & \lambda_{\mathcal{T}}Y \end{array}$$

$$\bar{H}: \lambda_{\mathcal{S}}X \times I \to \lambda_{\mathcal{T}}Y,$$

that can be obtained by extending for each $t \in I$, *the map* $H_t: H \mid X \times \{t\}$, *as is defined in* II.4.5.

PROOF

Thus $\bar{H}$ is defined by:

$$\bar{H}(M,t) = \underline{\{T\in\mathcal{T} \mid H_t^{-1}T\in M\}}.$$

We only have to prove continuity. Suppose $(M,t) \in \lambda_S X \times I$ and $T_0 \in T$ and

$$\bar{H}(M,t) \notin T_0^+.$$

Then, because $\{T \in T \mid H_t^{-1} T \in M\}$ is a pre-mls for $\bar{H}(M,t)$,

$$\exists T_1 \in T \quad H_t^{-1} T_1 \in M \quad \text{and} \quad T_1 \cap T_0 = \emptyset$$

Choose $T_0', T_1' \in T$ such that $T_1' \cap T_0' = Y$

and

$$T_i' \cap T_i = \emptyset, \quad i = 1,2.$$

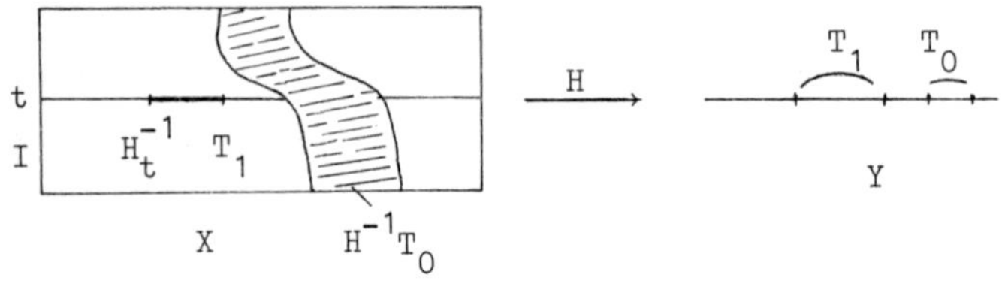

Because X is compact

$$\exists \varepsilon > 0 \quad H_t^{-1}(Y \setminus T_1') \times (t-\varepsilon, t+\varepsilon) \cap H^{-1} T_0 = \emptyset.$$

It is easily seen that

$$(H_t^{-1}(Y \setminus T_1'))^+ \times (t-\varepsilon, t+\varepsilon)$$

is an open neighbourhood of (M,t) in $\lambda_S X \times I$, that is disjoint of $(H^{-1}T_0)^+$.

II.5. EXTRA CONDITIONS ON THE SUBBASE S

In this section we study the implications of S being (weakly) normal or closed under algebraic operations such as the taking of (finite) unions and/or intersections, for the structure of mls's in $\lambda_S X$ or in $\beta_S X$ (an for the separation axioms). Important applications are on λX and on $\lambda_Z(X)$ and $\beta_Z(X)$ where Z is the family of zerosets of X, which is then supposed to be completely regular.

First we study the relation between prime mls's (i.e. mls's in $\beta_S X$, cf. I.5.2 and II.1.7) and (maximal) centered systems, if S is weakly normal.

II.5.1. PROPOSITION

A prime centered system M in a weakly normal family S is a pre-mls.

PROOF

Suppose $T, T' \in \mathcal{S}$ and $T \cap T' = \emptyset$. Then there exist $S_1, \ldots, S_n \in \mathcal{S}$ such that

$$S_1 \cup \ldots S_n = X$$

$$S_i \text{ meets at most one of } T \text{ and } T', \quad i = 1, \ldots, n.$$

Because M is prime $\exists i \in \{1, \ldots, n\}$ $S_i \in M$. So not both T and T' meet all elements of M, i.e. M is a pre-mls (cf. I.1.9.a).

II.5.2. THEOREM

If $\mathcal{S}$ is weakly normal then for $M \in \lambda_{\mathcal{S}}X$ the following conditions are equivalent

(i) $M \in \beta_{\mathcal{S}}X$

(ii) M *is prime*

(iii) M *contains a maximal centered system.*

PROOF

(i) $\Longleftrightarrow$ (ii) by II.1.7 and (iii) $\Longrightarrow$ (ii) by I.5.2 (vi) and II.1.7. Now suppose (ii). By II.1.7 M contains a prime centered system, say M'. Let M_1 be any maximal centered system in $\mathcal{S}$, which contains M', and M_2 any mls, which contains M_1. Because M' is a pre-mls, by II.5.1, $M = M_2 \supset M_1$. This proves (iii).

II.5.3. EXAMPLES

Notice that though a maximal centered system in a weakly normal subbase $\mathcal{S}$ uniquely determines an mls in $\beta_{\mathcal{S}}(X)$ (by II.5.1 and I.5.2.vi), it is not generally true that an mls from $\beta_{\mathcal{S}}(X)$ contains only one maximal centered system. The following examples show some of the possible relations between maximal centered systems and (prime) mls's (cf. I.1.8.d and I.5). But let us first introduce some notation on the Wallman-type-compactification.

If $\mathcal{S}$ is a subbase for the closed sets of a T_1-space X, then the *Wallman-type-$\mathcal{S}$-compactification* of X is denoted by $\omega_{\mathcal{S}}(X)$, i.e.:

$$\omega_{\mathcal{S}}(X) = \{M \mid M \text{ is an mcs in } \mathcal{S}\}.$$

Here *mcs* = maximal centered (sub)system. And if

$$S^* = \{M\in\omega_{\mathcal{S}}(X) \mid S\in M\} \qquad \text{for } S \in \mathcal{S}$$

then $\{S^* \mid S\in\mathcal{S}\}$ is a subbase for the closed sets of $\omega_{\mathcal{S}}(X)$. Observe that for $S_1,\dots,S_n \in \mathcal{S}$

$$\omega_{\mathcal{S}}(X)\backslash(S_1^*\cup\dots S_n^*) = \{M\in\omega_{\mathcal{S}}(X) \mid \exists T_1,\dots,T_k\in M$$
$$T_1\cap\dots T_k\subset(X\backslash S_1)\cap\dots(X\backslash S_n)\}.$$

So if we define $O^{\wp}$ for $O \subset X$ by

$$O^{\wp} = \{M\in\omega_{\mathcal{S}}(X) \mid \exists T_1,\dots,T_k\in M \quad T_1\cap\dots T_k\subset O\}$$

then $\{O^{\wp} \mid X\backslash O\in\mathcal{S}\}$ is an open subbase for $\omega_{\mathcal{S}}(X)$. Moreover

$$O_1^{\wp} \cap O_2^{\wp} = (O_1\cap O_2)^{\wp}.$$

Returning to the superextension we recall the following definition, for a set Y:

$$P_f(Y) = \{Y'\subset Y \mid Y' \text{ is finite}\}$$

and

$$P_{cof}(Y) = \{Y'\subset Y \mid Y\backslash Y' \text{ is finite}\}.$$

Let

$$X = A \cup B \cup C$$

be the union of three disjoint, infinite, fixed sets A, B and C. First we will define T_1-families $\mathcal{S}_1$, $\mathcal{S}_2$, $\mathcal{S}_3$, $\mathcal{S}_4$ of subsets of X (closed subbases for the discrete topology) such that:

$\mathcal{S}_1$ contains an mcs, that is not a pre-mls (so $\mathcal{S}_1$ is not weakly normal).

$\mathcal{S}_2$ is normal, so each mcs is a pre-mls. $\mathcal{S}_2$ contains three free mcs's: C_1, C_2 and C_3. While C_1 and C_2 are also maximally linked, C_3 is properly contained in the mls $\underline{C}_3$.

$\mathcal{S}_3$ is a normal family such that $\omega_{\mathcal{S}_3}(X)$ is Hausdorff. There are three free mcs's in $\mathcal{S}_3$, the union of which is the only free prime mls in $\mathcal{S}_3$.

S_4 is closed under the taking of finite unions, which implies that each mcs in S_4 is an mls (cf. II.5.5). So $\omega_S(X) \subset \beta_S(X)$. Yet $\omega_S(X) \neq \beta_S(X)$.

S_1

Put $S_1 = \{\{x\} \mid x\in X\} \cup \{(A\cup B)\setminus\{x\},(A\cup C)\setminus\{x\} \mid x\in X\} \cup \{B\cup\{a_1,a_2\},C\cup\{a_3,a_4\}\}$

where a_1,a_2,a_3,a_4 are different points in A. The free mcs's in S_1 are:

$$C_1 = \{(A\cup B)\setminus\{x\},(A\cup C)\setminus\{x\} \mid x\in X\}$$

$$C_2 = \{B\cup\{a_1,a_2\}\} \cup \{A\cup B\setminus\{x\} \mid x\in X\}$$

$$C_3 = \{C\cup\{a_3,a_4\}\} \cup \{A\cup C\setminus\{x\} \mid x\in X\}.$$

The free, prime mls's in S_1 are:

$$M_1 = C_1 \cup C_2$$

and

$$M_2 = C_1 \cup C_3.$$

S_1, as a (sub)base for the closed sets, induces the discrete topology on X. The subspaces $A \cup \{C_1\}$, $B \cup \{C_2\}$ and $C \cup \{C_3\}$ of $\omega_{S_1}(X)$ are the one-point-compactification of A, B and C respectively. The space $\omega_{S_1}(X)$ is the topological sum of these spaces, and is consequently Hausdorff. However, $\beta_{S_1}(X)$ is not Hausdorff: a neighbourhood of M_1 (M_2) consists of M_1 and all but finitely many points of $A \cup B$ (respectively M_2 and all but finitely many points of $A \cup C$). Observe that S_1 is not weakly normal: $B \cap C = \emptyset$, $B,C \in S_1$ but there are no $S_1,\ldots,S_n \in S$ with union X such that each S_i meets at most one of B and C.

S_2

Put $S_2 = \{\{x\} \mid x\in X\} \cup P_{cof}(X) \cup P_{cof}(A\cup C) \cup P_{cof}(B\cup C) \cup \{A,B,A\cup B\}.$

Observe that if $S,T \in S_2$ are disjoint, then one of them, say S, is either a singleton, or equals A or equals B. Then $(X\setminus S) \in S_2$, which shows that S_2 is normal. The free mcs's in S_2 are:

$$C_1 = P_{cof}(X) \cup \{A,A\cup B\} \cup P_{cof}(A\cup C),$$

$$C_2 = P_{cof}(X) \cup \{B,A\cup B\} \cup P_{cof}(B\cup C),$$

and

$$C_3 = P_{cof}(X) \cup P_{cof}(A\cup C) \cup P_{cof}(B\cup C).$$

The free, prime mls's in S_2 are $M_1 = C_1$, $M_2 = C_2$ and

$$M_3 = \underline{C}_3 = C_3 \cup \{A\cup B\}.$$

Now $\omega_{S_2}(X)$ and $\beta_{S_2}(X)$ are homeomorphic to $\omega_{S_1}(X)$. It is also worthwhile to observe that in $\beta_{S_2}(X)$

$$(A\cup B)^+ \cap \beta_{S_2}(X) = A \cup B \cup \{M_1,M_2,M_3\}$$

while

$$(A\cup B)^- = A \cup B \cup \{M_1,M_2\}.$$

S_3

Put $\quad S_3 = \{\{x\} \mid x\in X\} \cup P_{cof}(A\cup B) \cup P_{cof}(A\cup C) \cup P_{cof}(B\cup C) \cup P_{cof}(X).$

Again, if two sets $S,T \in S_3$ are disjoint, then one of them is a singleton, say $S = \{x\}$, and $(X\backslash S\in S_3)$ shows that S_3 is normal. The free mcs's in S_3 are:

$$C_1 = P_{cof}(X) \cup P_{cof}(A\cup B) \cup P_{cof}(A\cup C)$$

$$C_2 = P_{cof}(X) \cup P_{cof}(B\cup A) \cup P_{cof}(B\cup C)$$

$$C_3 = P_{cof}(X) \cup P_{cof}(C\cup A) \cup P_{cof}(C\cup B).$$

And

$$M_3 = C_1 \cup C_2 \cup C_3 = S_3\backslash\{\{x\} \mid x\in X\}$$

is the only free (prime) mls in S_3. Again $\omega_{S_3}(X)$ is homeomorphic to $\omega_{S_1}(X)$, while $\beta_{S_3}(X)$ is the one-point-compactification of X, obtained by the identification $C_1 = C_2 = C_3$ in $\omega_{S_3}(X)$. In particular both $\omega_{S_3}(X)$ and $\beta_{S_3}(X)$ are Hausdorff.

S_4

Let $C = C' \cup C''$, where C' and C'' are disjoint and infinite. Put (for '$A^{Ⓕ}$' see II.4.5)

$$S_4 = (\{A\cup B, B\cup C', A\cup C\}\cup P_{cof}X)^{Ⓕ} \cup \{\{x\} \mid x\in X\}$$

$$= \cup\{P_{cof}Y \mid Y = A,B,C',A\cup B,A\cup C',B\cup C'\} \cup \{\{x\} \mid x\in X\}.$$

Recall that each mcs in S_4 is an mls, because $S_4 = S_4^{Ⓕ}$. The only three free mcs's in S_4 are:

$$M_1 = \cup\{P_{cof}Y \mid Y = A, A\cup B, A\cup C', X\}$$

$$M_2 = \cup\{P_{cof}Y \mid Y = B, A\cup B, B\cup C', X\}$$

$$M_3 = \cup\{P_{cof}Y \mid Y = C', A\cup C', B\cup C', X\}$$

and the only other free mls in S is:

$$M_4 = \cup\{P_{cof}Y \mid Y = A\cup B, A\cup C', B\cup C', X\}.$$

If $S_1, \ldots, S_n \in S$ and $S_1 \cup \ldots S_n = X$ then at least one $S_i \in P_{cof}X$, and this S_i belongs to all free mls's. So all mls's are prime, i.e. $\lambda_S(X) = \beta_S(X) = X^- \neq \omega_S(X) = X \cup \{M_1, M_2, M_3\}$.

A similar example is obtained by letting $X = \mathbb{N} \cup \{a,b,c\}$ be the T_1-space consisting of a pointsequence ($\mathbb{N}$) converging to three different points (a, b and c). Then X is compact, and so $\omega_G(X) = X$. However $\beta_G(X)$ also contains the mls

$$\{S\in G \mid S \text{ contains at least two points of a, b, c}\},$$

and is a pointsequence converging to four points.

Finally we give, for illustration of theorem II.5.4, a more topological example viz. of a normal T_1-subbase S_5 for the same X such that $\omega_{S_5}(X)$ is not Hausdorff, while $\beta_{S_5}(X)$ of course is Hausdorff.

S_5

Let c_1, c_2, c_3 be three different fixed points in C. Put

$$S_5 = \{\{x\} \mid x\in X\} \cup P_{cof}(X) \cup$$
$$\cup \{A'\cup\{c_i,c_j\} \mid A'\in P_{cof}(A),\ i\neq j,\ i,j\in\{1,2,3\}\}$$
$$\cup \{B'\cup\{c_i,c_j\} \mid B'\in P_{cof}(B),\ i\neq j,\ i,j\in\{1,2,3\}\}.$$

Then S_5 contains two free mcs's, viz.

$$C_1 = P_{cof}(X) \cup \{A'\cup\{c_i,c_j\} \mid \ldots\}$$

and

$$C_2 = P_{cof}(X) \cup \{B'\cup\{c_i,c_j\} \mid \ldots\}.$$

A basic neighbourhood of C_1 or C_2 in $\omega_{S_5}(X)$ contains all but finitely many points of C (and all but finitely many points of A, respectively B), so $\omega_{S_5}(X)$ is not Hausdorff. Because S_5 contains only one mls, viz.

$$M = C_1 \cup C_2 = S_5 \setminus \{\{x\} \mid x \in X\}.$$

$\beta_{S_5}(X)$ is the (Hausdorff) one-point-compactification of X, that can be obtained from $\omega_{S_5}(X)$ by identification of C_1 and C_2.

Let us finally observe that in all cases there are no other mls's, i.e.

$$\lambda_{S_i}(X) = \beta_{S_i}(X) \qquad \text{for } i = 1,2,3,4,5.$$

II.5.4.

Above we saw that there is a canonical map i: $\omega_S(X) \to \beta_S(X) \subset \lambda_S(X)$ if S is weakly normal. We will show that this is a (closed) continuous map:

THEOREM

If S is a weakly normal T_1-subbase for X, *then* $\beta_S(X)$ *is a Hausdorff quotient of* $\omega_S(X)$ *under the continuous canonical map* i: $\omega_S(X) \to \beta_S(X)$ *defined by*

$$i(M) = \underline{M}.$$

(Recall that M is a pre-mls and $\underline{M}$ denotes the unique mls containing M, cf. II.5.2, I.1.5).

REMARK

This theorem is historically the basis of the notion of linked systems, superextensions and supercompactness. If S is a weakly normal subbase that is closed under the taking of finite intersections, then $\omega_S X$ is Hausdorff and thus X must be completely regular. However if the algebraic condition ($S = S^{(f)}$) is dropped, then $\omega_S X$ need not be Hausdorff any more. In trying to characterize complete regularity De Groot and Aarts observed at this point that a Hausdorff-quotient, now called $\beta_S X$, can be obtained from $\omega_S X$ by identification of those $M, N \in \omega_S X$ for which $M \cup N$ is linked. Because X is still embedded in this quotient, again X must be $T_{3\frac{1}{2}}$. This method naturally lead to the definition of superextension and supercompactness.

PROOF

Because S is weakly normal $\beta_S(X)$ is Hausdorff (II.3.3). So we only have to prove continuity. We use the notation of II.5.3 above for $\omega_S X$. Suppose $S \in S$ and $M \in \omega_S(X) \setminus i^{-1}(S^+)$, i.e. $M \cup \{S\}$ is not linked, then $\exists T \in M$ $T \cap S = \emptyset$. Choose $S_1, \ldots, S_n \in S$ such that

$$S_1 \cup \ldots S_k \cup \ldots S_n = X,$$

$$S \subset S_1 \cup \ldots S_k \subset X \setminus T,$$

and

$$T \subset S_{k+1} \cup \ldots S_n \subset X \setminus S.$$

Clearly no S_l with $l \leq k$ belongs to M. So the basic open set

$$\omega_S(X) \setminus (S_1^* \cup \ldots S_k^*)$$

contains M. We claim that this set is disjoint from $i^{-1}S$. For suppose $N \in \omega_S(X) \setminus S_1^* \cup \ldots S_k^*$. Because N is maximally centered and $S_1 \cup \ldots S_n = X$, some S_l, necessary with $k < l \leq n$, must belong to N. Now this S_l is disjoint from S, so $N \notin i^{-1}(S)$.

Next we discuss the consequences of some algebraic conditions for S. Especially we look for conditions under which different subbases produce "the same" superextensions. First we recall our notation. For an arbitrary family A we put:

$$A^{\cap} = \{A \mid \exists A' \subset A \quad A = \cap A' \quad \text{and} \quad A' \neq \emptyset\} \cup \{\cup A'\}$$

$$A^{\cup} = \{A \mid \exists A' \subset A \quad A = \cup A'\}$$

$$A^{\textcircled{f}\cap} = \{A \mid \exists n \in \mathbb{N} \quad A_1, \ldots, A_n \in A \quad A = A_1 \cap \ldots A_n\}$$

$$A^{\textcircled{f}\cup} = \{A \mid \exists n \in \mathbb{N} \quad A_1, \ldots, A_n \in A \quad A = A_1 \cup \ldots A_n\}$$

We say that A is *closed under (the taking of)* (finite) unions if $A = A^{\cup}$ ($A = A^{\textcircled{f}\cup}$ respectivelt) etc. Observe that if the subbase S really is a base (e.g. if $S = S^{\textcircled{f}\cup}$) that then $S^{\cap} = G$ = the family of all closed sets.

II.5.5. PROPOSITION

If $S = S^{\textcircled{f}\cap}$, *then each maximal centered system is an mls, and*

$$i(X) \subset \omega_S(X) \subset \beta_S(X) \subset \lambda_S(X).$$

If moreover $\beta_S X$ *is Hausdorff (e.g.* S *is weakly normal), then*

$$\omega_S(X) = \beta_S(X).$$

PROOF

The inclusions in the first part are trivial. The second part follows from the compactness of $\omega_S X$ (cf. II.5.2 and II.5.4). Without weak normality equality need not hold, as we saw in II.5.3 with S_4.

II.5.6. THEOREM

If X *is compact and* $S = S^{(f)} \subset T \subset S^{\cap}$*, then* T *is a closed* T_1*-subbase for* X *and the maps*

$$\lambda_{S^{\cap}}(X) \longrightarrow \lambda_T(X) \longrightarrow \lambda_S(X)$$

$$M \longmapsto M \cap T \longmapsto M \cap S$$

are homeomorphisms that commute with the embeddings of X.

PROOF

Clearly T is a closed subbase for X. We show that T is T_1: if $x \in X$ and $T \in T$, $S' \subset S$ satisfy $x \notin T = \cap S'$, then $\exists S' \in S'$ such that $x \notin S'$. Because S is T_1, $\exists S \in S \subset T \quad x \in S \subset (X\backslash S') \subset (X\backslash T)$.

Next we show that each $M \in \lambda_S(X)$ is a pre-mls in T. Suppose $S_i \subset S$ and $S_i = \cap S_i$ meets all $S \in M$, $i = 1,2$. Then $S_1^{(f)} \subset M$ and $S_2^{(f)} \subset M$. Hence $S_1^{(f)} \cup S_2^{(f)}$ is linked, but then it is centered and has a non-empty intersection because X is compact. I.e. $S_1 \cap S_2 \neq \emptyset$.

Finally we have to show that the map $M \mapsto \underline{M}$ (to be denoted by $h: \lambda_S(x) \to \lambda_T(x)$) is a homeomorphism, i.e. is 1-1, onto, $h^{-1}T^+$ is closed for each $T \in T$ and $h(S^+)$ is closed for each $S \in S$.

h is 1-1: If $M \neq N$ in $\lambda_S(X)$, then $M \cup N$ is not linked (cf. I.1.2), so $\underline{M} \neq \underline{N}$.

h is onto: If $M \in \lambda_T(X)$ and $N = M \cap S$, then we claim that N is maximally linked. Suppose $S \in S\backslash M$. Then $\exists S' \subset S \quad (\cap S') \in M$ and $(\cap S') \cap S = \emptyset$. Because S is compact $\exists S_1,\ldots,S_n \in S' \quad S_1 \cap \ldots S_n \cap S = \emptyset$. Clearly

$(\cap\mathcal{S}') \subset S_1 \cap \ldots S_n \in \mathcal{M} \cap \mathcal{S} = \mathcal{N}$, so $\mathcal{N} \cup \{S\}$ is not linked.

h is continuous. If $T \in \mathcal{T}$, say $\mathcal{S}' \subset \mathcal{S}$ and $T = \cap\mathcal{S}'$, then

$$h^{-1}(T^+) = \cap\{h^{-1}(S^+) \mid S \in \mathcal{S}'^{\textcircled{f}}\}.$$

Inclusion is obvious, so suppose $\mathcal{M} \in \lambda(\mathcal{S})\backslash h^{-1}(T^+)$. Then apparently $\exists S' \in \mathcal{M}$ $S' \cap T = \emptyset$. Because S' is compact $\exists S \in \mathcal{S}'^{\textcircled{f}}$ $S \cap S' = \emptyset$. I.e. $\mathcal{M} \notin h^{-1}(S^+)$.

h^{-1} is continuous. If $S \in \mathcal{S}$, then obviously

$$h(S^+) = S^+$$

(where the first $^+$ is taken in $\lambda(\mathcal{S})$ and the second in $\lambda(\mathcal{T})$), because $\forall \mathcal{M} \in \lambda(\mathcal{S}) \quad \mathcal{M} = h(\mathcal{M}) \cap \mathcal{S}$.

From the above proof it is clear that we may sharpen II.5.6 as follows:

II.5.7. COROLLARY 1

If $\mathcal{S}$ *is a* T_1*-subbase for the space* X *and* $\mathcal{T}$ *satisfies*

(i) $\mathcal{S} \subset \mathcal{T} \subset \mathcal{S}^{\cap}$

(ii) $\forall T \in \mathcal{T} \exists S \in \mathcal{S} \quad T \subset S$ *and* S *is compact and*

(iii) $\forall T \in \mathcal{T} \forall S_1, S_2 \in \mathcal{S} \exists S_3 \in \mathcal{S} \quad T \subset S_1 \cap S_2 \Longrightarrow T \subset S_3 \subset S_1 \cap S_2$

then the map

$$\lambda_{\mathcal{T}}(X) \longrightarrow \lambda_{\mathcal{S}}(X)$$

$$\mathcal{M} \longmapsto \mathcal{M} \cap \mathcal{S}$$

is a homeomorphism that commutes with the embeddings of X.

The following corollary applies e.g. to the case X compact, T_2 and $\mathcal{S} = \mathcal{Z}$ is the family of all zerosets of X.

II.5.8. COROLLARY 2

If X *is compact,* $\mathcal{S} = \mathcal{S}^{\textcircled{f}} = \mathcal{S}^{\textcircled{\cup}}$ *, and* $\mathcal{T}$ *is any family of closed sets containing* $\mathcal{S}$ *then the maps*

$$\lambda(X) \longrightarrow \lambda_{\mathcal{T}}(X) \longrightarrow \lambda_{\mathcal{S}}(X)$$

$$\mathcal{M} \longmapsto \mathcal{M} \cap \mathcal{T} \longmapsto \mathcal{M} \cap \mathcal{S}$$

are homeomorphisms that commute with the embeddings of X.

Here the compactness of X is essential. We give two examples:

First let X be a (non-compact) Tychonoff-space which is not normal, and $\mathcal{Z}$ the family of all zerosets of X, and $\mathcal{G} = \mathcal{Z}^{\cap}$ the family of all closed subsets of X. Then, by II.5.4 and II.4.4.i:

$$\beta_{\mathcal{Z}}(X) = \omega_{\mathcal{Z}}(X) \cong \beta(X)$$

while

$$\beta_{\mathcal{G}}(X)$$

is not even Hausdorff (see 3.3 (iii) and cf. 4.2).

Secondly we show that even if $X = \mathbb{N}$ and $\mathcal{S} = P_f(\mathbb{N}) \cup P_{cof}(\mathbb{N})$, a normal T_1-subbase, then an mls M in $\mathcal{S}$ need not be a pre-mls in $\mathcal{S}^{\cap}$. Put $M = P_{cof}(\mathbb{N}) \in \lambda(\mathcal{S})$. Then any of the $2^{\underline{c}}$ free maximal centered systems in $P(\mathbb{N})$ is an mls in $P(\mathbb{N})$ and contains M.

From II.4.5 we know that for all T_1-spaces, compact and non-compact, we have:
If $\mathcal{S} \subset \mathcal{T}$ are two T_1-subbases for X, and $\mathcal{S}$ is normal, then the map

$$f: \lambda_{\mathcal{T}}(X) \to \lambda_{\mathcal{S}}(X)$$

$$f(M) = M \cap \mathcal{S}$$

is a continuous surjective extension of $id_{i(X)}$.
We now define:
If $\mathcal{T}_1$ and $\mathcal{T}_2$ are two families of subsets of a set X, then $\mathcal{T}_1$ is *normally screening* $\mathcal{T}_2$ iff

$$\forall T_2, T_2' \in \mathcal{T}_2 \, \exists T_1, T_1' \in \mathcal{T}_1 \quad T_2 \cap T_2' = \emptyset \Longrightarrow$$
$$T_1 \cup T_1' = X \quad \text{and} \quad T_1 \cap T_2 = T_1' \cap T_2' = \emptyset.$$

II.5.9. REMARKS

(i) $\mathcal{S}$ normally screens $\mathcal{S}$ iff $\mathcal{S}$ is a normal family.

(ii) The family $\mathcal{Z}$ of zerosets of X normally screens the family of all closed sets $\mathcal{G}$ iff X is normal.

(iii) If $\mathcal{S} \subset \mathcal{S}' \subset \mathcal{T}$ and $\mathcal{S}$ normally screens $\mathcal{T}$ then

S and T are normal,
S normally screens S', and
S' normally screens T.

(iv) If $S \subset T$ are subbases for the T_1-space X and S normally screens T, then, by (iii) & De Groot-Aarts' characterization II.3.5, X is completely regular. Moreover, by Zorn's lemma, there is a maximal subbase T', containing T, which is normally screened by S.

Both theorem II.5.6 and the following theorem mention conditions on two subbases $S \subset T$ for a T_1-space X of a certain class, such that $\lambda_T X$ and $\lambda_S X$ are homeomorphic under the canonical map

$$M \mapsto M \cap S$$

While II.5.6 applies to compact T_1-spaces and has an algebraic condition on S, viz. $S = S^{\text{ⓕ}}$, the next theorem applies to all $T_{3\frac{1}{2}}$-spaces and uses the more geometric condition of normal screening.

II.5.10. THEOREM

If $S \subset T$ are T_1-subbases for X and S normally screens T, then the map

$$\lambda_T(X) \longrightarrow \lambda_S(X)$$

$$M \longmapsto M \cap S$$

is a homeomorphism, that commutes with the embeddings of X. Moreover $\lambda_S(X)$ and $\lambda_T(X)$ are Hausdorff and X is completely regular.

PROOF

The last part of the theorem follows from II.5.9.iv. Define $f: \lambda_T(X) \to P(S)$ by $f(M) = M \cap S$. We claim that $f: \lambda_T(X) \to \lambda_S(X)$, i.e. $M \cap S \in \lambda(S)$ if $M \in \lambda(T)$. Clearly $M \cap S$ is linked, suppose $S \in S \backslash M$. Then $\exists T \in M \quad S \cap T = \emptyset$. Because S normally screens T, and $S,T \in T \quad \exists S',T' \in S$

$$S' \cup T' = X$$

and

$$S \cap S' = T \cap T' = \emptyset.$$

Clearly $T' \notin M$, so $S' \in M \cap S$, and $M \cup \{S\}$ is not linked.

Next we claim that each $M \in \lambda(S)$ is a pre-mls in T; this shows that f is bijective. Suppose $T,T' \in T$ both meet all $S \in M \in \lambda(S)$, but $T \cap T' = \emptyset$. Because S normally screens T,

$$\exists S,S' \in S \quad S \cup S' = X$$

$$S \cap T = S' \cap T' = \emptyset.$$

At least one of S and S' belongs to M. Contradiction.

Because $\lambda_S X$ and $\lambda_T X$ are compact Hausdorff there only remains to observe that f is continuous. This is trivial because $\forall S \in S \quad f^{-1}(S) = S^+ = \{M \in \lambda(T) \mid S \in M\}$.

II.5.11.

An analogous result is obtained for $\beta_S(X)$ and $\beta_T(X)$ if we start from II.4.6, and replace "normal screening" by the weaker condition of "weakly normal screening", which is defined next. The simple proofs are omitted because of their resemblance to the above. If T_1 and T_2 are two families of subsets of a set X then T_1 is *weakly normally screening* T_2 if for every two disjoin $T',T'' \in T_2$, there exist finitely many $T_1,\ldots,T_n \in T_1$ covering X, none of which meets both T' and T".

II.5.12. REMARKS (Analogous to II.5.9)

(i) S weakly normally screens S iff S is weakly normal.

(ii) If S weakly normally screens T, then $S^{\mathfrak{P}}$ normally screens T.

(iii) If $S \subset S' \subset T$ and S weakly normally screens T then S also does so with S', and S' with T.

(iv) If $S \subset T$ are subbases for the T_1-space X, and S weakly normally screens T, then (by (iii) and II.3.5) X is completely regular. Moreover, by Zorn's lemma, there is a maximal, closed subbase T' containing T which is weakly normally screened by S.

II.5.13. THEOREM

If $S \subset T$ are T_1-subbases for X *and S weakly normally screens T, then the map*

$$\beta_T(X) \longrightarrow \beta_S(X)$$
$$M \longmapsto M \cap S$$

is a homeomorphism that commutes with the embeddings of X. *Moreover* $\beta_T(X)$ *and* $\beta_S(X)$ *are Hausdorff and* X *is completely regular.*

II.5.14.

The next focus of interest is the relation between the closure of i(S) in $\lambda_S(X)$, $i(S)^-$, and S^+, or rather $S^+ \cap i(X)^- = S^+ \cap \beta_S(X)$, for $S \in S$. Clearly

$$S^- \subset S^+ \cap \beta_S(X).$$

E.g. II.5.3 $-S_2$ and the following example show that even if S satisfies very nice conditions, then equality need not hold.

EXAMPLE (Cf. [7], ex. 4, p. 104).

Let $X = \mathbb{N}$, $S = P_f(\mathbb{N}) \cup \{A \in P_{cof}\mathbb{N} \mid 1 \in A \text{ or } 2 \in A\}$. Then $S = S^{\mathfrak{L}}$ and S is a normal base for the closed sets of N with the discrete topology.

The only free maximal centered system in S is $S \setminus P_f(\mathbb{N})$, because a free maximal centered system never contains finite sets. By II.5.2 the only prime mls (= mls in $\beta_S X$) is $\overline{S \setminus P_f(\mathbb{N})} = (S \setminus P_f \mathbb{N}) \cup \{A \in P_f \mathbb{N} \mid \{1,2\} \subset A\}$. Name this mls M_∞, and identify $\mathbb{N}$ with $i(\mathbb{N})$, then

$$\{1,2\}^- = \{1,2\} \subsetneq \{1,2\}^+ = \{1,2,M_\infty\}.$$

As immediate consequence of II.5.5 we have

II.5.15 PROPOSITION

If $S = S^{\mathfrak{f}}$, *then* $\forall S \in S \quad i(S)^- = S^+ \cap \beta_S(X)$.

The following proposition gives a necessary and sufficient but rather complicated condition for a $S \in S$ to satisfy $i(S)^- = S^+ \cap \beta_S(X)$. The trivial proof is omitted.

II.5.16. PROPOSITION

For $S \in \mathcal{S}$ $(S)^- = S^+ \cap \beta_{\mathcal{S}}(X)$ *iff for each finite cover,* $S \subset S_1 \cup \ldots S_n$, *of* S *by elements of* $\mathcal{S}$, *and for each prime mls* M, $S \in M \Longrightarrow \exists i \quad S_i \in M$.

If we consider the superextension of $\lambda_{\mathcal{S}}(X)$ with respect to $\{S^+ \mid S \in \mathcal{S}\}$ then this is (canonically homeomorphic to) $\lambda_{\mathcal{S}}(X)$ again, because this is a binary subbase (cf. II.2.3). Also the superextension of $\beta_{\mathcal{S}}(X)$ with respect to $\{S^+ \cap \beta_{\mathcal{S}}(X) \mid S \in \mathcal{S}\}$ is easily seen to be homeomorphic to $\lambda_{\mathcal{S}}(X)$ under the canonical map

$$M \mapsto \{S^+ \cap \beta_{\mathcal{S}}(X) \mid S \in M\}.$$

This shows

II.5.17. THEOREM

Every superextension of X *can be regarded as the superextension of a compactification of* X, *viz.*

$$\lambda_{\mathcal{S}} X = \lambda_{\mathcal{S}'} \beta_{\mathcal{S}} X$$

where

$$\mathcal{S}' = \{S^+ \cap \beta_{\mathcal{S}} X \mid S \in \mathcal{S}\}.$$

II.6. SUPEREXTENSIONS AND GRAPHS

II.6.1.

Several problems and results can be clarified by replacing the subbase $\mathcal{S}$ by the graph that is its nerve. Then mls's in $\mathcal{S}$ correspond to complete subgraphs of the nerve and for $S \in \mathcal{S}$ (a point in the graph) S^+ is the family of all complete subgraphs that contain S. However if $\mathcal{S}$ is not closed under suitable algebraic operations, then it seems hard to re-obtain from the nerve information about inclusion, intersections and unions of elements of $\mathcal{S}$.

A short sketch of the framework of this translation is presented in this section.

II.6.2.

DEFINITIONS

A *graph* is an ordered pair (V,S) that satisfies:

(i) V is a set, the elements of which are called *vertices*.

(ii) S is a set of two element subsets of V, whose elements are called *sides*.

The two vertices that belong to a side are called the *endpoints* of this side.

If no confusion is likely then we may write V for the pair (V,S).

If $\mathcal{T}$ is any family of sets then *nerve* $\mathcal{T}$ is defined as a graph whose vertices represent the elements $T \in \mathcal{T}$, and whose sides correspond to those two element sets $\{T,T'\} \subset \mathcal{T}$ for which $T \cap T' \neq \emptyset$.

A graph (V,S) is *complete* if $S = \{\{p,q\} \mid p,q\in V,\ p\neq q\}$. A graph (V,S) is a *subgraph* of a graph (V',S') if $V \subset V'$ and $S \subset S'$. If (V,S) is a graph and $p \in V$ then we define

$$p^+ = \{(V',S') \mid (V',S') \text{ is a maximal complete subgraph of } (V,S) \text{ and } p\in V'\}.$$

The *superextension of a graph* (V,S), denoted by

$$\lambda(V,S)$$

is the topological space, the points of which are the maximal complete subgraphs of (V,S), and for which a subbase for the closed sets is given by

$$\{p^+ \mid p\in V\}.$$

A graph (V,S) is *normal* if for any $p,q \in V$ $\{p,q\} \notin S$ implies $\exists p',q' \in V$ such that

$$\{p,p'\} \notin S$$
$$\{q,q'\} \notin S$$

and every maximal complete subgraph contains p' or contains q'.

II.6.3. REMARK

In defining notions corresponding to normality and primeness one problem it is impossible to tell from the nerve of $\mathcal{S}$ whether or not a certain finite subfamily of S covers $\cup S = X$. E.g. if S is a T_1-subbase for a space X and $\beta_S(X) \neq \lambda_S(X)$, then we may choose $M \in \lambda_f(S)\backslash\beta_S(X)$ and $S_1,\ldots,S_n \in S$ such that $S_1,\ldots,S_n \notin M$ but $X \subset S_1 \cup \ldots S_n$. So $\exists T_1,\ldots,T_n \in M \quad T_i \cap S_i = \emptyset$, $i = 1,\ldots,n$. Now adjoin one isolated point p to X:

$$Y = X \cup \{p\}$$

and put

$$S' = (S\backslash M) \cup \{S\cup\{p\} \mid S\in M\}.$$

Then S' is a T_1-subbase for the T_1-space Y, and nerve S' = nerve S. However $S_1,\ldots,S_n \in S \cap S'$ cover X but do not cover Y.

If S satisfies the condition (called *strongly T_1*) $\forall p \in X$
$\forall S_1,\ldots,S_n \in S \quad p \notin S_1 \cup \ldots S_n \Longrightarrow \exists T \in S \quad p \in T \subset X\backslash(S_1\cup\ldots S_n)$
then
$\forall S_1,\ldots,S_n \in S$ ($S_1 \cup \ldots S_n = X$ iff each point of nerve S is connected by a side to some S_i).

This leads to the following definition:
A set V' of vertices is *prime* in a graph (V,S) if for each finite number of vertices $p_1,\ldots,p_n \in V$ $(\forall r\in V \quad \exists i\in\{1,\ldots,n\} \quad \{p_i,r\}\in S) \Longrightarrow \exists i \in \{1,\ldots,n\}$ $p_i \in V'$

II.6.4. PROPOSITION

(i) *If S contains all singletons of* X *or S is a T_1-subbase and $S = S^{\text{fi}}$, then S is strongly T_1.*

(ii) *If S is a strongly T_1-subbase for* X *then the prime maximal complete subgraphs of S correspond to the prime mls's in S i.e. to $\beta_S(X)$. Moreover each side of* (V,S) *is contained in a prime maximal complete subgraph.*

II.6.5. PROPOSITION

Let S be a T_1-subbase for a T_1-space X *and* $i(X) \subset Y \subset \lambda_S(X)$, $S(Y) = \{S^+\cap Y \mid S\in S\}$. *If* (V,S) *is the nerve of* X *and* (V_y,S_y) *the nerve of* $S(Y)$, *then* $\lambda(V,S)$, $\lambda(V_y,S_y)$, $\lambda_S(X)$ *and* $\lambda_{S(Y)}(Y)$ *are canonically homeomorphic. (Also* $S(Y)$ *is a T_1-subbase for* Y*).*

II.6.6. PROPOSITION

If (V,S) *is a graph, then*

(i) λ(V,S) *is a supercompact* T_1*-space,*

(ii) $\{p^+ \mid p \in V\}$ *is a binary, closed* T_1*-subbase for* λ(V,S),

(iii) *nerve* $\{p^+ \mid p \in V\}$ = (V,S),

(iv) *if* (V,S) *is a normal graph, then* λ(V,S) *is Hausdorff.*

The simple proofs of II.6.4-6 are omitted.

II.6.7. EXAMPLES

(i) Consider the nerve of the family of proper subsets of {1,2,3}:

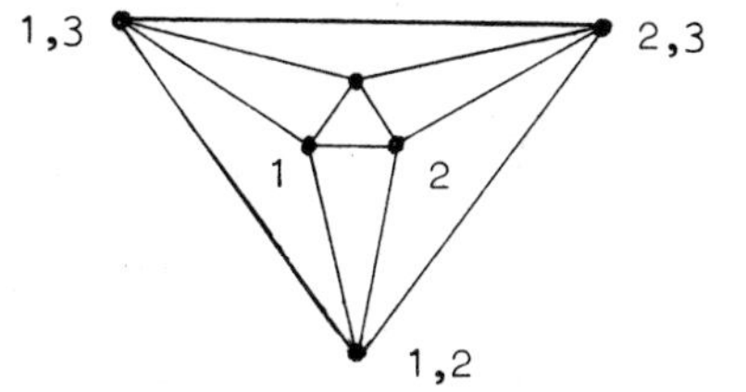

The maximal complete subgraphs are

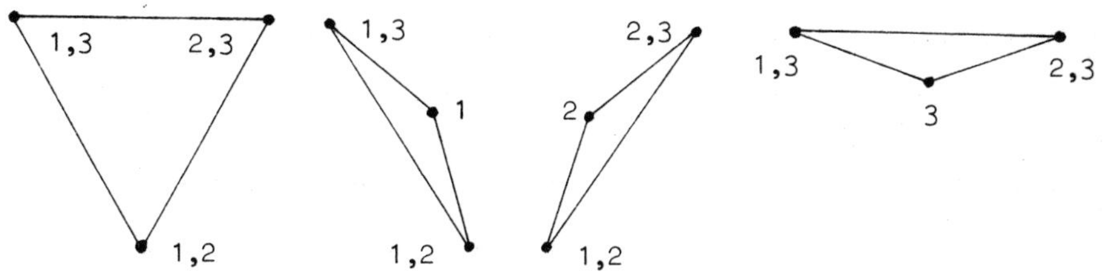

(ii) Consider the λP{1,2,3,4,5}. If an mls contains a four-point-set as minimal set, then it is of type (5,4) as is easily seen. So all other free mls's only have two- and three-point-sets for minimal sets. Consider the dual graph of the nerve of the family of two- and three-point-sets in {1,2,3,4,5}, i.e. the graph with the same vertices, but the complementary family of sides

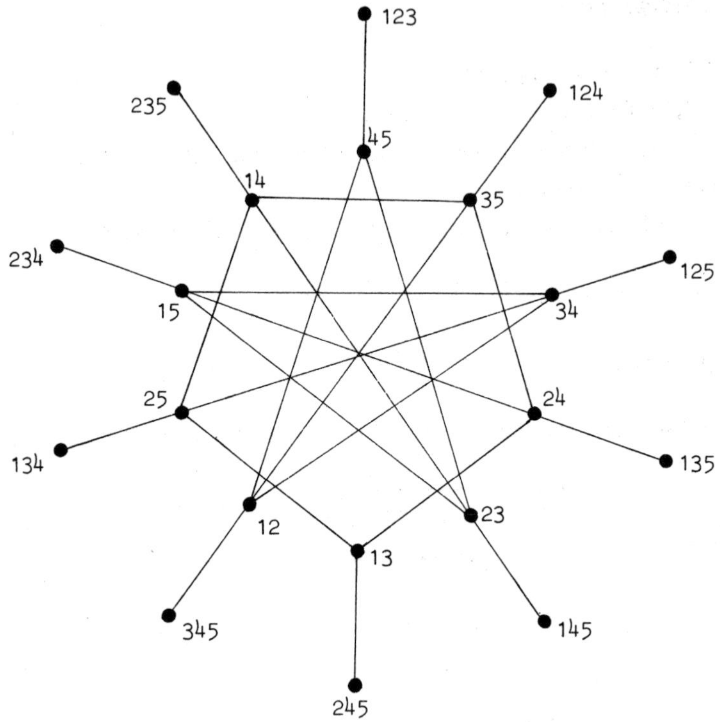

In this graph mls's correspond to maximal sets of (pairwise) unconnected vertices. It is easy to see that (up to symmetry) there are five types:
the mls's of type (4,1),
the (one) mls of type (5,1) which consists of all three-element-sets, and

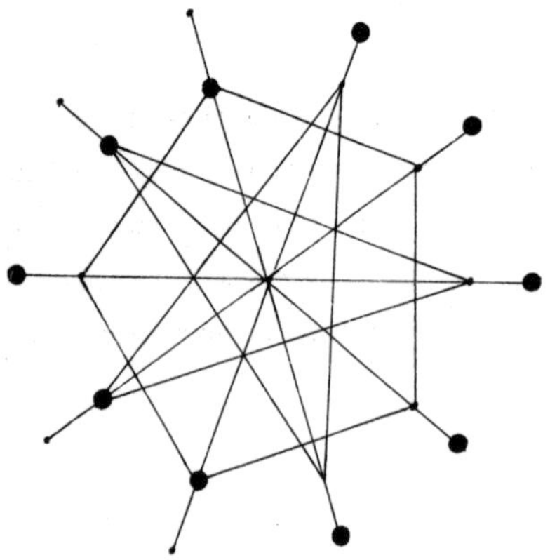

corresponding to the fixed mls i(1) (type (1,1))

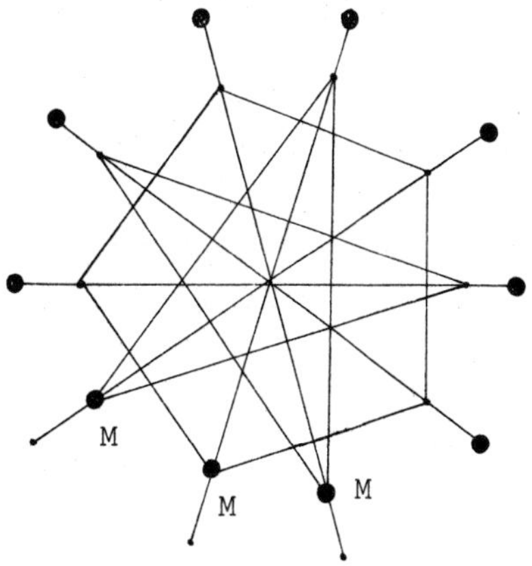

corresponding to the pre-mls {{1,2},{1,3},{2,3}}, of type (3,1) (vertices corresponding to minimal sets are indicated by M)

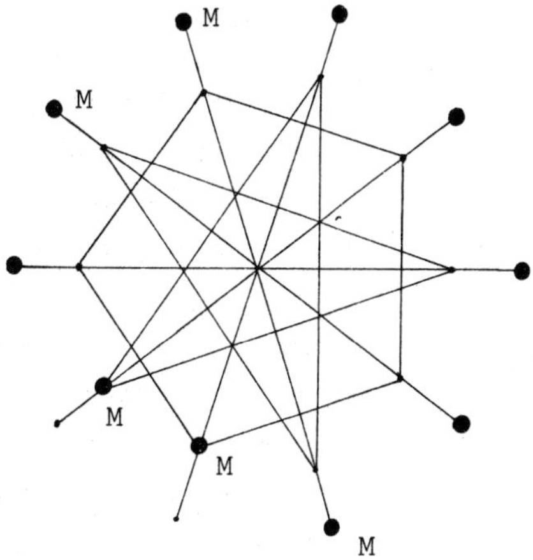

corresponding to type (5,3)

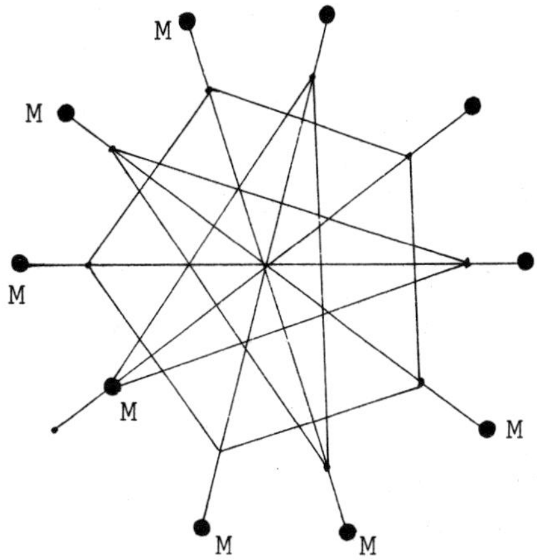

corresponding to type (5,2)

CHAPTER III MORE TOPOLOGICAL PROPERTIES OF SUPEREXTENSIONS

> Si les plats que je vous offre sont mal préparés, c'est moins la faute de mon cuisinier, que celle de la chemie, qui est encore dans l'enfance.
>
> (La Rôtisserie de la reine Pédauque - Anatole France)

In this chapter the investigation is proceeded of the superextensions $\lambda_S X$ of a T_1-space X relative a T_1-subbase S. First we are concerned with "cardinal functions", viz. weight and dimension (in section one) and density and the Suslin number (in section three). Here separability is equivalent to countable density. With the exception of the dimension these cardinal functions are the same for $\lambda_S X$ and X under certain mild conditions. The dimension of $\lambda_S X$ is, roughly speaking, mostly either zero or strongly infinite (see III.1.4 and V.1). Other topological invariants that are discussed are: connectedness and contractibility. The two main theorems of this chapter deal with these properties. Let us for simplicity only mention the results for λX, the superextension with respect to all closed sets. First, after a development of the necessary machinery in section two, we prove in III.4.1 that λX is connected and locally connected if and only if X is connected. Secondly for a class of (pseudo) compact, connected spaces, including all finite polyhedra, λX is shown to be contractible (III.4.3).

III.1. WEIGHT AND DIMENSION

III.1.1. DEFINITIONS

The *weight* of X, w(X) is the minimal cardinality of a (sub)base of X.
X is *0-dimensional* if X has a (sub)base of sets that are both open and closed. (Hence X is $T_{3\frac{1}{2}}$).
X is *strongly 0-dimensional* if for each closed $G \subset X$ and each open $O \subset X$ with $G \subset O$, there exists an open-and-closed $L \subset X$ such that $G \subset L \subset O$.
X is *$\geq$1-dimensional* if X is $T_{3\frac{1}{2}}$, but not a 0-dimensional.
X is strongly *∞-dimensional* if X is $T_{3\frac{1}{2}}$, but not the union of countably many 0-dimensional subsets.

III.1.2. THEOREM (G.A. JENSEN, [9])

If X *is compact, Hausdorff, and* S *is either a normal* T_1*-subbase or* $S = S^{(\cap)} = S^{(f)}$, *then*

$$w(X) = w(\lambda_S X) = w(\lambda X).$$

PROOF

First we show that $w(X) = w(\lambda X)$. Let $\mathcal{B} = \mathcal{B}^{(\cup)}$ be an open base for X of cardinality $w(X)$. Then for $M \neq N$, mls's in λX, there exist $S \in M$, $T \in N$ with $S \cap T = \emptyset$. By the compactness of X $\exists U,V \in \mathcal{B}$ $S \subset U$, $T \subset V$ and $U \cap V = \emptyset$, (because $\mathcal{B} = \mathcal{B}^{(\cup)}$). So if $\{O^+ \mid O \in \mathcal{B}\}$ is taken as open subbase for λX, then it induces a Hausdorff topology which clearly is contained in (= weaker than) the superextension topology. So these topologies coincide, i.e. $\{O^+ \mid O \in \mathcal{B}\}$ is an open subbase for λX, and consequently $w(\lambda X) \leq w(X)$.

If S is a normal T_1-subbase or $S = S^{(\cap)} = S^{(f)}$, then $\lambda_S(X)$ is a (closed, continuous) image of λX (by II.4.5 CORO 1) or $\lambda_S X$ is homeomorphic to λX respectively (by II.5.8). Hence $w(\lambda_S X) = w(\lambda X)$.

III.1.3. COROLLARY

If X *is a* T_1*-space and* S *is a normal* T_1*-subbase then* $w(\lambda_S X) = w(\beta_S X)$.

PROOF

$\beta_S X$ is a Hausdorff quotient of the closure of $i(X)$ in $\lambda(X)$ by II.4.6 CORO, and $\lambda_S = \lambda_{S'} \beta_S X$ by II.5.17.

III.1.4. REMARKS

(i) Theorem III.1.2 has no obvious equivalent for local weight - just as in the case of the hyperspace -. This is shown in V.1, by the example of the superextension of the Alexandroff double of a circle.

(ii) It is easily seen that compactness is essential, e.g. the superextension of the natural numbers, $\mathbb{N}$, contains their Čech-Stone compactification, $\beta\mathbb{N}$.

III.1.4. THEOREM (Cf. G.A. Jensen [9])

(a) *If* X *is 0-dimensional and* $\mathcal{S}$ *is a subbase consisting of closed-and-open sets, and* S ∈ $\mathcal{S}$ ⟹ (X\S) ∈ $\mathcal{S}$, *then* $\lambda_{\mathcal{S}}(X)$ *is 0-dimensional.*

(b) λX *is 0-dimensional iff* X *is strongly 0-dimensional.*

(c) *If* X *contains an interval then* λX *is strongly* ∞*-dimensional.*

REMARKS

(i) Theorems II.5.6 - II.5.13 combined with (a) and (b) above imply 0-dimensionality for a number of superextensions $\lambda_{\mathcal{T}}(X)$, for different T_1-subbases $\mathcal{T}$, by showing that $\lambda_{\mathcal{T}}(X)$ is homeomorphic to $\lambda_{\mathcal{S}}(X)$ or λX above.

(ii) In IV we will see that for a compact, metrizable space X, λX is either 0-dimensional (if X is) or else strongly ∞-dimensional.

PROOF

(a) By II.1.6 $\{(X\backslash S)^+ \mid S \in \mathcal{S}\}$ is an open subbase for $\lambda_{\mathcal{S}}X$. However for S ∈ $\mathcal{S}$ also (X\S) ∈ $\mathcal{S}$, and so $(X\backslash S)^+$ is open-and-closed.

(b) If-part. If $\mathcal{S}$ is the family of all open-and-closed sets, then $\mathcal{S}$ normally screens the family of all closed sets because X is strongly 0-dimensional. By (a) $\lambda_{\mathcal{S}}(X)$ is 0-dimensional and by II.5.10 $\lambda_{\mathcal{S}}(X)$ and λX are homeomorphic.

Only-if-part. If λX is 0-dimensional, and hence Hausdorff, then X is normal and the closure of X is the Čech-Stone βX. So βX is 0-dimensional and hence X is strongly 0-dimensional. (Of course a simple direct proof also exists.)

(c) Assume [-1,1] ⊂ X. We define a pre-mls $\mathcal{M}$ in $P(\mathbb{Z})$ as we did in I.1.8.d:

$$\mathcal{M} = \{\{-n,0,1,2,\dots,n-1\} \mid n \in \mathbb{N}\} \cup$$
$$\cup \{\{-1,-2,-3,\dots,-n,n\} \mid n \in \mathbb{N}\} \cup$$
$$\cup \{\{0,1,2,3,\dots\}\}.$$

Observe that

(*) $\underline{\mathcal{M}} = \{S \subset \mathbb{Z} \mid \exists T \in \mathcal{M} \quad T \subset S\}$.

Choose for $n < 0$, disjoint, non-degenerate, closed intervals J_n in $[-1,0)$. We will define a 1-1, continuous $f\colon \Pi\{J_n \mid n<0\} \to \lambda X$ which shows that λX contains a copy of the Hilbertcube and thus is strongly ∞-dimensional. This map is obtained by defining an mls in λX, defined on $\{\ldots,p_{-2},p_{-1},0,1,1/2,1/3,\ldots\}$ of the same type as M, and "letting the points p_n roam a litttle in J_n" (for $n<0$). We define for $p = (p_n)_n \in \Pi\{J_n \mid n<0\}$:

$$g_p\colon Z \to [-1,1]$$

by

$$g_p(k) = \begin{cases} 1/k & \text{if } k > 0, \\ p_k & \text{if } k < 0, \text{ and} \\ 0 \quad \text{(or anything else)} & \text{if } k = 0 \end{cases}$$

and further $f(p) = \{S \in G \mid g_p^{-1}(S) \in \underline{M}\}$.
(In the terminology of II.4.5 $f(p) = \bar{g}_p(\underline{M})$, cf. I.2.7 or III.2.2). It is easily seen that $f(p) \in \lambda X$ and f is 1-1. Notice that $S \in f(p)$ either contains a finite set (viz. $\{p_n,1,1/2,1/3,\ldots,1/(n-1)\}$ or $\{p_1,p_2,p_3,\ldots,p_n,1/n\}$ for some $n \in N$), or contains $g_p\{1,2,3,\ldots\}^- = \{0,1,1/2,1/3,\ldots\}$. For the proof of the continuity of f, assume $0 \in O$ and

$$f(p) \in O^+.$$

Then, by (*), $\exists S \in (f(p))_{MIN}$ $\quad S \subset O$.
Now if $S = \{0,1,1/2,1/3,\ldots\}$ then $f(p) \in O^+$ for all p, and else S is finite. In the latter case

$$\cap\{\pi_i^{-1}(O \cap J_i) \mid p_i \in S \text{ and } i<0\}$$

(where $\pi_i\colon \Pi\{J_n \mid n<0\} \to J_i$ is the projection map), is an open neighbourhood of p that is mapped by f into O^+.

III.2. MAPPING PRODUCTS AND HYPERSPACES INTO $\lambda_S X$

III.2.1.

The following condition is presupposed throughout the following three sections in order to apply some results of I.2. Roughly stated it guarantees the existence of enough fmls's.

In III.2,3,4 *THE SUBBASE* S *CONTAINS ALL FINITE SUBSETS OF* X. *IN FORMULA*

$$P_f X \subset S.$$

III.2.2.

Suppose $M \subset P\{1,\dots,n\}$ is an mls and $(x_1,\dots,x_n) \in X^n$ is a finite sequence of n, not necessarily different points in X. Then

$$\{\{x_j \mid j\in S\} \mid S\in M\}$$

is a pre-mls in S. Indeed, this family obviously is linked, and if $T \in S$ meets all $\{x_j \mid j\in S\}$ for $S \in M$, then $T' = \{i \mid x_i\in T\}$ meets all $S \in M$, and hence $T' \in M$. Now $\{x_i \mid i\in T'\} \subset T$. We define fmls $(M,x_1,\dots,x_n)$ in $\lambda_S X$ by:

(i) $$(M,x_1,\dots,x_n) = \underline{\{\{x_j \mid j\in S\} \mid S\in M\}} = \{T\in S \mid \{j \mid x_j\in T\}\in M\}.$$

Observe that if we let $f\colon \{1,\dots,n\} \to \{x_1,\dots,x_n\}$ be the "index map": $f(i) = x_i$, then

(ii) $$(M,x_1,\dots,x_n) = \bar{f}(M)$$

where $\bar{f}$ is defined as in I.2.7. However, here we are more interested in keeping M fixed, and varying $x_1,\dots,x_n$. So we define

(iii) $$f_M\colon X^n \to \lambda_S X$$

by

$$f_M((x_1,\dots,x_n)) = (M,x_1,\dots,x_n).$$

From I.2.7 we see that

(iv) $$\text{Image } f_M = \{N\in\lambda_S X \mid N \text{ is an fmls and type } N \leq \text{type } M\}.$$

Moreover if M is minimally defined on $\{1,\dots,n\}$ then

(v) type (M) = type $((M,x_1,\dots,x_n))$ iff $x_1,\dots,x_n$ are pairwise different.

The next proposition, III.2.5, claims that this map is continuous - if X^n

is endowed with the product topology -. Moreover, as intuitively is clear, f_M is a local homeomorphism in each point $(x_1,\dots,x_n) \in X^n$ for which all x_i are different, i.e. on a dense subset, at least if X is Hausdorff. However if not all x_i are different and $\{x_1,\dots,x_n\} = \{y_1,\dots,y_n\}$ then $(M,x_1,\dots,x_n)$ and $(M,y_1,\dots,y_n)$ may or may not be equal, depending on the type of M. From the scheme in I.2.10 we may read of, for $n \leq 6$, some of the identifications that the map $f_M\colon X^n \to \lambda_S X$ makes. This scheme also illustrates clearly how much more complicated the image of X^n is, then e.g. the nth symmetrical product of X. Because of the importance of the construction of $(M,x_1,\dots,x_n)$ first two examples are presented.

III.2.3. EXAMPLE

Let $X = \mathbb{R}$ be the real line and $S = G$ the family of all closed subsets in $\mathbb{R}$. Let

$$M = \underline{\{\{1,2\},\{1,3\},\{2,3\}\}} \in \lambda\mathbb{R} \qquad \text{(type } M = \text{type } (3,1))$$

and

$$N = \underline{\{\{2,3,4\},\{1,2\},\{1,3\},\{1,4\}\}} \in \lambda\mathbb{R} \qquad \text{(type } N = \text{type } (4,1))$$

Now for $(x_1,x_2,x_3) \in \mathbb{R}^3$

$$f_M((x_1,x_2,x_3)) = (M,x_1,x_2,x_3) =$$

$$= \{S\in S \mid S \text{ contains } x_i \text{ for at least two } i\in\{1,2,3\}\}$$

If $x_i = x_j$ for $i \neq j$ then $f_M((x_1,x_2,x_3))$ is the fixed mls with intersection x_j. Moreover f_M maps $\{(x_1,x_2,x_3) \in \mathbb{R}^3 \mid x_1<x_2<x_3\}$ homeomorphically and densely into the image $f_M(R^3)$. So $f_M \mid \{(x_1,x_2,x_3)\in\mathbb{R}^3 \mid x_1\leq x_2\leq x_3\}$ is irreducible. We will show that

this f_M is not a quotientmap.

Put $G = \{(x,y,z)\in R^3 \mid xy=1 \text{ and } z=0\}$. Recall that $i\colon \mathbb{R} \to \lambda\mathbb{R}$ is the canonical embedding. Now

$$\{(-\varepsilon,\varepsilon)^+ \mid \varepsilon>0\}$$

is a neighborhoodbasis of $i(0)$ in $\lambda\mathbb{R}$. For each $\varepsilon > 0$, we can find an $(x,\frac{1}{x},0) \in G$ such that

$$\{0,1/x\} \subset (-\varepsilon,\varepsilon),$$

whence

$$f_M((x,1/x,0)) \in (-\varepsilon,\varepsilon)^+.$$

This shows that

$$i(0) \in f_M(\mathbb{R}^3) \cap f_M(G)^-\backslash f_M(G).$$

Because G is closed in $\mathbb{R}^3$ and $f_M^{-1}f_MG$ is a finite union of three isometric copies of G, $f_M^{-1}f_MG$ is also closed in $\mathbb{R}^3$. However f_MG is not closed in $f_M\mathbb{R}^3$, so f_M is not a quotient map.

The structure of N is less symmetric than the structure of M. We have:

$$f_N\colon \mathbb{R}^4 \to \lambda_4(\mathcal{S})$$

$$f_N((x_1,x_2,x_3,x_4)) = \begin{cases} i(x_1) \text{ if } x_1 = x_i \text{ for } i \in \{2,3,4\} \\ f_M((x_1,x_2,x_3)) \text{ if } x_3 = x_4 \text{ or } x_2 = x_4 \\ f_M((x_1,x_2,x_4)) \text{ if } x_2 = x_3 \\ i(x_2) \text{ if } x_2 = x_3 = x_4 \\ \{S\in\mathcal{S} \mid S\supset\{x_2,x_3,x_4\} \text{ or} \\ (x_1\in S \text{ and } \{x_2,x_3,x_4\}\ S\neq\emptyset)\} \text{ if all } x_i \text{ are} \\ \text{different.} \end{cases}$$

Thus f_N cannot be factored over the fourth symmetrical product of $\mathbb{R}^4$ because e.g.

$$f_N((0,1,2,3)) \neq f_N((1,2,3,0)) = f_N((1,0,2,3)).$$

III.2.4. LEMMA

The function $f_M\colon X^n \to \lambda_{\mathcal{S}}X$ *defined in III.2.2 satisfies*

(a) *If* $A \subset X$ *then*

$$f_M^{-1}(A^+) = \bigcup_{S\in M} \left(\bigcap_{i\in S} \pi_i^{-1}A\right)$$

(where $\pi_i\colon X^n \to X$ *is the* i^{th} *projection map).*

(b) *If* $A_1,\ldots,A_n \subset X$ *then*

$$f_M(A_1 \times \ldots A_n) \subset \bigcap_{S\in M} (\bigcup_{i\in S} A_i)^+.$$

(c) *If* $A_1,\ldots,A_n \subset X$ *are disjoint and* M *is an n-mls, then*

(i) $\bigcap_{S\in M} (\bigcup_{i\in S} A_i)^+ \cap \lambda_f(S) \subset \{N\in\lambda_f(S) \mid \text{type } M \leq \text{type } N\}$

and

(ii) $f_M \mid A_1 \times \ldots A_n$ *is 1-1 and has the following image:*

$$\bigcap_{S\in M} (\bigcup_{i\in S} A_i)^+ \cap \lambda_n(S).$$

PROOF

(a) The following equivalences hold:

$$f_M((x_1,\ldots,x_n)) \in A^+ \iff$$

$$\iff \exists S \in M \quad \{x_i \mid i\in S\} \subset A \iff$$

$$\iff \exists S \in M \quad (x_1,\ldots,x_n) \in \cap\{\pi_i^{-1}A \mid i\in S\}.$$

(b) If $(a_1,\ldots,a_n) \in A_1 \times \ldots A_n$ and $S \in M$ then

$$f_M((a_1,\ldots,a_n)) = (M,a_1,\ldots,a_n) \ni \{a_i \mid i\in S\} \subset \cup\{A_i \mid i\in S\}$$

so

$$f_M((a_1,\ldots,a_n) \in (\cup\{A_i \mid i\in S\})^+.$$

(c) (i) Let $g: A_1 \cup \ldots A_n \to \{1,\ldots,n\}$ be defined by

$$g(a) = i \quad \text{if} \quad a \in A_i.$$

If $N \in \bigcap_{S\in M} (\bigcup_{i\in S} A_i)^+ \cap \lambda_f(S)$ then $\bar{g}(N)$ is defined in I.2.7 by

$$\bar{g}(N) = \{S\subset\{1,\ldots,n\} \mid g^{-1}(S)\in N\}$$

and we have: type $\bar{g}(N) \leq$ type N.
Obviously $\bar{g}(N) = M$.

(c) (ii) Injectivity. Suppose $(a_1,\ldots,a_n),(a_1',\ldots,a_n') \in A_1 \times \ldots A_n$ and $f_M((a_1,\ldots,a_n)) = f_M((a_1',\ldots,a_n'))$. Then this mls is an n-mls (by III.2.2.v) and its smallest defining set is $\{a_1,\ldots,a_n\} = \{a_1',\ldots,a_n'\}$. Because the A_i are disjoint, this implies $\{a_i\} = A_i \cap \{a_1,\ldots,a_n\} = A_i \cap \{a_1',\ldots,a_n'\} = \{a_i'\}$, $(i=1,\ldots,n)$. Moreover $f_M((a_1,\ldots,a_n)) \in \bigcap_{S\in M} (\bigcup_{i\in S} A_i)^+$ by (b).

Surjectivity. Suppose $N \in \bigcap_{S\in M} (\bigcup_{i\in S} A_i)^+ \cap \lambda_n(S)$. Then by (i) type $(M) \leq$ type (N) and because both are n-mls's, even type (M) = type (N) must hold. Suppose N is minimally defined on $\{x_1,\ldots,x_n\}$. First we claim that $A_j \cap \{x_1,\ldots,x_n\} \neq \emptyset$ (and hence = a singleton) for each $j = 1,\ldots,n$. Choose $S,T \in M$ such that $S \cap T = \{j\}$, which is possible because M is minimally defined on $\{1,\ldots,n\}$. Then because

$$N \in (\cup\{A_i \mid i\in S\})^+ \cap (\cup\{A_i \mid i\in T\})^+,$$

we obtain:

$$\exists N,N' \subset \{x_1,\ldots,x_n\} \quad N,N' \in N$$

and

$$N \subset \cup\{A_i \mid i\in S\}, \quad N' \in \cup\{A_i \mid i\in T\}.$$

So

$$\emptyset \neq N \cap N' \subset \cup\{A_i \mid i\in S\} \cap \cup\{A_i \mid i\in T\} = A_j,$$

which proves our claim. Now re-index $(x_1,\ldots,x_n)$ in such a way that

$$x_i \in A_i \qquad\qquad (i=1,\ldots,n).$$

Then $(x_1,\ldots,x_n) \in A_1 \times \ldots A_n$ and we claim that

$$f_M((x_1,\ldots,x_n)) = N,$$

or equivalently $\{x_i \mid i\in S\} \in N$ for each $S \in M$. This is trivial because

1. N is defined on $x_1,\ldots,x_n$
2. $N \in (\cup\{A_i \mid i\in S\})^+$ for each $S \in M$.
3. $(\cup\{A_i \mid i\in S\}) \cap \{x_1,\ldots,x_n\} = \{x_i \mid i\in S\}$.

III.2.5. PROPOSITION

If $M \in \lambda P\{1,\ldots,n\}$ *and* $f_M\colon X^n \to \lambda_S(X)$ *is defined (as in III.2.2) by*

$$f_M((x_1,\ldots,x_n)) = \{S\in S \mid \{i \mid x_i\in S\}\in M\}$$

then

(a) f_M *is continuous*

(b) *Image* $f_M = \{N\in\lambda_f(S) \mid \text{type } N \leq \text{type } M\}$.

If X *is Hausdorff, then moreover*

(c) *Image* f_M *is closed in the subspace* $\lambda_f(S)$.

(d) f_M *is a local homeomorphism in each point* $(x_1,\ldots,x_n) \in X^n$ *for which all* x_i *are different, if* M *is an n-mls.*

As an immediate consequence of (b) and (c) we may observe the following:

COROLLARY

If X *is Hausdorff, then the following sets are closed in the subspace* $\lambda_f(S)$ *of* $\lambda_S(X)$:

(i) $\lambda_n(S)$ *for any* $n \in \mathbb{N}$,

(ii) $\{N\in\lambda_f(S) \mid \text{type } N \leq \text{type } M\}$ for every $M \in \lambda_f(S)$.

PROOF

(a) follows from III.2.4.a.

(b) was observed in III.2.2.v.

(c) Let $N \in \lambda_f(S)\backslash\text{Image } f_M$. Suppose N is minimally defined on $x_1,\ldots,x_k$ and $A_1,\ldots,A_k$ are pairwise disjoint open neighbourhoods of $x_1,\ldots,x_k$ respectively. Then by III.2.4.c(i) the following neighbourhood of

$$\cap\{(\bigcup_{i\in S} A_i)^+ \mid S\in N_{MIN}\}$$

contains only mls's of type $\geq$ type N, and hence no mls's of type $\leq$ type M.

(d) If $(x_1,\ldots,x_n) \in X^n$ and all x_i are different and X is Hausdorff, then we may choose pairwise disjoint open neighbourhoods O_i of x_i, $i=1,\ldots,n$. By III.2.4.c $f_M \mid O_1 \times \ldots O_n$ is 1-1 and continuous. Moreover for any basic open set $U_1 \times \ldots U_n$ in $O_1 \times \ldots O_n$, again by III.2.4.c

$$f_M(U_1\times\ldots U_n) = f_M(O_1\times\ldots O_n) \cap \bigcap_{S\in M} (\bigcup_{i\in S} U_i)^+$$

is a basic, relatively open set in $f_M(O_1\times\ldots O_n)$. Hence $f_M \mid O_1 \times \ldots O_n$ is a homeomorphism.

III.2.6. PROPOSITION

Let $g\colon \lambda_f(S) \times \lambda_f(S) \times \lambda_f(S) \to P(S)$ *be defined (as in I.1.3.e) by*

$$g(M,N,P) = (M \cap N) \cup (N \cap P) \cup (P \cap M)$$

Then (i) *if* $M = P$, *then* $g(M,N,P) = M$

(ii) Image $g = \lambda_f(S)$

(iii) $g \mid \{M\} \times \{N\} \times \lambda_f(S)$ *is a retraction*

$\lambda_f(S) \to \cap\{S^+ \mid S \in M \cap N\} \cap \lambda_f(S)$

(iv) $g: \lambda_f(S)^3 \to \lambda_f(S)$ *is a continuous surjection*

(v) *if* $M,N \in A_1^+ \cap \ldots A_k^+$ *then* $\forall P \in \lambda_f(S)$

$g(M,N,P) \in A_1^+ \cap \ldots A_k^+$.

PROOF

(i) is trivial and shows the $\supset$-part of (ii). For the $\subset$-part of (ii), suppose that $(M,N,P) \in \lambda_f(S)^3$ and that M, N and P are defined on the finite sets M, N and P respectively. Consequently

$$\forall S \in g(M,N,P)\ \exists T \in g(M,N,P) \qquad T \subset S \cap (M \cup N \cup P).$$

Moreover we claim that

$(*)$ $\forall T \subset M \cup N \cup P$ either $T \in g(M,N,P)$ or $(M \cup N \cup P) \backslash T \in g(M,N,P)$.

From these two formula's together with I.2.2.iv one easily deduces that $g(M,N,P) \in \lambda_f(S)$. Proof of $*$: let $T \subset M \cup N \cup P$. If T belongs at least two of M, N and P then $T \in g(M,N,P)$ and we are done. So suppose $T \notin M$ and $T \notin N$. I.e. $(M \backslash T) \in M$ and $(N \backslash T) \in N$ and so $(M \cup N \cup P) \backslash T \in$ $\in M \cap N \subset g(M,N,P)$.

(iii) Continuity follows from (iv). If $P \in \lambda_f(S)$ then obviously $M \cap N \subset g(M,N,P)$, so $g(M,N,P) \in \cap\{S^+ \mid S \in M \cap N\}$. If $P \in \cap\{S^+ \mid S \in M \cap N\}$, then $P \supset M \cap N$, so

$$g(M,N,P) = (M \cap N) \cup (N \cap P) \cup (M \cap P) \subset P,$$

and hence $g(M,N,P) = P$.

(iv) Continuity follows immediately from the trivial formula

$$\forall S \in S \quad g^{-1}(S^+) = \lambda_f(S)^3 \cap (\lambda_f(S) \times S^+ \times S^+ \cup S^+ \times \lambda_f(S) \times S^+ \cup S^+ \times S^+ \times \lambda_f(S)).$$

(v) If $M, N \in A_1^+ \cap \ldots A_k^+$ then there exist finite sets $S_i \in M$, $T_i \in N$ such that $S_i \subset A_i$ and $T_i \subset A_i$, $i = 1,\ldots,k$. So

$$g(M,N,P) \ni S_i \cup T_i \subset A_i \qquad (i=1,\ldots,k)$$

i.e. $g(M,N,P) \in A_i^+ \qquad (i=1,\ldots,k)$.

III.2.7. PROPOSITION

If $M \in \lambda_m(S)$ *and* $M' \in \lambda_{m'}(S)$, $A_1,\ldots,A_k \subset X$ *and* $M,M' \in A_1^+ \cap \ldots A_k^+$ *then there is a continuous map*

$$f\colon\ X^{mm'} \to \lambda_f(S) \cap A_1^+ \cap \ldots A_k^+$$

that contains both M *and* M' *in its image.*

REMARK

If X is not connected then this is a triviality, but if X is connected it will turn out to be very powerful.

PROOF

By I.2.9.d there exists an mls N defined on $\{1,2,\ldots,mm'\}$ and points $(x_1,\ldots,x_{mm'}) \in X^{mm'}$ and $(x_1',\ldots,x_{mm'}') \in X^{mm'}$ such that (for def. see III.2.2)

$$(N,x_1,\ldots,x_{mm'}) =_{\text{def}} \underline{\{\{x_i \mid i\in S\} \mid S\in N\}} = M$$

and

$$(N,x_1',\ldots,x_{mm'}') = M'.$$

Now define $f\colon X^{mm'} \to \lambda_f(S)$ as follows:

$$f((y_1,\ldots,y_{mm'})) = g(M,M',(N,y_1,\ldots,y_{mm'}))$$

where g is defined as in III.2.6. The required properties of f immediately follow from III.2.6 and III.2.5.

III.2.8. HYPERSPACES OF PROPER CLOSED SUBSETS OF X IN λX.

First recall the definition of the hyperspace H(Y) of a topological space Y (cf. e.g. [14]):

the underlying set is $H(Y) = \{G \subset Y \mid G \text{ is closed}, G \neq \emptyset\}$ and a basis for the open sets consists of all sets

$$<O_1,\ldots,O_n> = \{G \in H(Y) \mid G \subset O_1 \cup \ldots O_n \text{ and } G \cap O_1 \neq \emptyset \text{ and } \ldots G \cap O_n \neq \emptyset\} \quad \text{for } O_1,\ldots,O_n \text{ open in } Y.$$

Next recall the mls defined in I.1.3.d: if $G \in H(X)$ (i.e. $G \in \mathcal{G}$ and $G \neq \emptyset$) and $p \in X$ then

$$M(p,G) = \{S \in \mathcal{G} \mid G \subset S \text{ or } (G \cap S \neq \emptyset \text{ and } p \in S)\}$$

is an mls, i.e. $M(p,G) \in \lambda X$. This defines a map $f\colon X \times H(X) \to \lambda X$ which will be shown to be continuous. Unfortunately, if $p \in G$ then f is not 1-1:

$$M(p,G) = i(p).$$

However if $p \notin G$ then the map f is a local homeomorphism in (p,G), at least if X is regular:

PROPOSITION

If $f\colon X \times H(X) \to \lambda X$ *is defined (as above) by*

$$f(p,G) = \underline{\{G,\{p,q\} \mid q \in G\}}$$

then f *is continuous. Moreover for each two disjoint closed subsets* Y *and* Z *of* X

$$f \mid Y \times H(Z)$$

is an embedding.

PROOF

Suppose $O \subset X$ is open and $f(p,G) \in O^+$. Then $\{p,q\} \subset O$ for some $q \in G$, or $G \subset O$. In the former case $O \times <O,X>$ is a neighborhood of (p,G) that is mapped by f into O^+. In the latter $X \times <O>$ plays this role.

Finally let Y and Z be disjoint closed subsets of X. Suppose $O \times <O_1,\ldots,O_n> \cap Y \times H(Z)$ is a basic open set in $Y \times H(Z)$. We may furthermore assume that $O \cap Z = \emptyset$ and $(O_1 \cup \ldots O_n) \cap Y = \emptyset$. Then it is easily seen that $f(O \times <O_1,\ldots,O_n> \cap Y \times H(Z)) = f(Y \times H(Z)) \cap (O \cup O_1)^+ \cap \ldots (O \cup O_n)^+ \cap (O_1 \cup \ldots O_n)^+$.

which shows that f is relatively open. As it is trivial that $f \mid Y \times H(Z)$ is 1-1, this completes the proof.

III.3. FMLS'S, DENSE SUBSETS AND THE CELLULARITY NUMBER

As in the previous section we assume that $P_f(X) \subset S$.

III.3.1. LEMMA

If $B_i \subset X$, $i = 1,\dots,k$ *and* $\{B_1,\dots,B_k\}$ *is linked then* $\exists \underline{M} \in \lambda_f(S)$, $\underline{M} \in B_1^+ \cap \dots B_k^+$.

PROOF

For $i,j = 1,\dots,k$ choose

$$b_{ji} = b_{ij} \in B_i \cap B_j.$$

Put $\underline{B}_i = \{b_{i1},\dots,b_{ik}\}$. Then $\{\underline{B}_1,\dots,\underline{B}_k\}$ is a linked family of finite sets. Let M be any mls in $P\{b_{ij} \mid i,j=1,\dots,k\}$ containing $\{\underline{B}_1,\dots,\underline{B}_k\}$. Then $\underline{M} \in \lambda_f(S) \cap B_1^+ \cap \dots B_k^+$.

III.3.2. COROLLARY 1

If $A_i \subset X$, $i=1,\dots,n$, *are arbitrary, then* $A_1^+\cap\dots A_n^+ \subset (A_1^+\cap\dots A_n^+\cap\lambda_f(S))^-$.

PROOF

Let $O_1^+ \cap \dots O_m^+$ be a basic open neighbourhood of $N \in A_1^+ \cap \dots A_n^+$. Then apply III.3.1. to $\{O_i,A_j \mid i,j\}$.

III.3.3. COROLLARY 2

If $D \subset X$ *is dense, then* $\{M\in\lambda_f(S) \mid M$ *is defined on* $D\}$ *is dense in* $\lambda_S X$.

PROOF

If $O_1^+ \cap \dots O_n^+$ is a basic open set, then apply III.3.1 to the linked family $\{O_i\cap D \mid i=1,\dots,n\}$, and observe that in III.3.1 M is defined on $A_1 \cup \dots A_n$.

III.3.4. THEOREM

If S is a closed subbase for the T_1-space X, and S contains all finite subsets of X then

$$(\lambda_f(S))^- = \lambda_S(X).$$

PROOF

Apply III.3.1 to a basic open set, i.e. $X\backslash B_i \in S$ for $i = 1,\dots,k$.

III.3.5. DEFINITION

The *density* of X, d(X), is the minimal cardinality of a dense subspace of X.

THEOREM

If S is a closed subbase for the T_1-space X and S contains all finite subsets of X, then

$$d(\lambda_S(X)) \leq d(X).$$

In particular $\lambda_S(X)$ is separable iff X is separable.

PROOF

Because for any infinite set $A \subset X$, there are card A many fmls's defined on A, III.3.5 follows immediately from III.3.3.

III.3.6. PROPOSITION

A subset A of a T_1-space X is nowhere dense in X iff A^+ is nowhere dense in λX.
(Cf. V.2.1).

PROOF

Only if. Let O_i be open in X, $i = 1,\dots,n$, and assume $O_1^+ \cap \dots O_n^+$ is a non-empty (basic open) set in λX. For each $i,j = 1,\dots,n$ put $O_{ij} = O_i \cap O_j \cap \cap (X\backslash A^-)$. Then O_{ij} is non-empty and open in X. Put $U_i = O_{i1} \cup \dots O_{in}$. It follows easily that $\{U_1,\ldots,U_n\}$ is linked, i.e.

$$\emptyset \neq U_1^+ \cap \ldots U_n^+ \subset O_1^+ \cap \ldots O_n^+ \backslash A^+.$$

If. Suppose A is not nowhere dense in X, i.e. $O \subset (A^-)$, for some non-empty open subset O of X. We will show that $O^+ \subset cl_{\lambda X}(A^+)$.

Suppose $M \in O^+$ and $O_1^+ \cap \ldots O_n^+$ is a basic open neighbourhood of M in λX. Then $\{O,A,O_1,\ldots,O_n\}$ is a linked family of subsets of X. Now by III.3.1 $A^+ \cap O_n^+ \cap \ldots O_n^+ \neq \emptyset$.

III.3.7. REMARK

Especially lemma III.3.2 but also theorems III.3.4 and III.3.5 show how densely the fmls's are sawn in $\lambda_S X$. They are not only dense in $\lambda_S X$ and consequently in any basic open set $O_1^+ \cap \ldots O_n^+$ but even in any intersection of finitely many 'plusses' of arbitrary subsets of X. On the other hand this shows how 'large' these finite intersections of plusses of subsets of X are. Yet they are not so large that III.3.6 does not hold, and that, for normal X, λX is not Hausdorff.

III.3.8. DEFINITION

The *cellularity number* or *Suslin number* of X, c(X), is defined as the supremum of the cardinalities of families of pairwise disjoint open sets.

REMARK

It may be appropriate to mention some properties of c(X). For proofs or further references see e.g. [11].

(i) X is said to enjoy the *Suslin-property* iff $c(X) = \aleph_0$. A *Suslin continuum* is a linearly ordered compact, connected, non-separable space with the Suslin-property.

(ii) It is consistent with the usual axioms of set-theory (e.g. with the Zermelo-Fraenkel-system + axiom of choice + general continuum hypothesis) to assume that there exists a Suslin-continuum. If C is any Suslin-continuum, then ('always')

$$c(C\times C) = \aleph_1 > c(C) = \aleph_0.$$

However it is also consistent to assume that no Susling-continuum exists, or equivalently, that each linearly ordered, compact, connected space with the Suslin-property is homeomorphic to a closed interval of real numbers.

(iii) If $c(X)$ is a singular cardinal, then there is a family of pairwise disjoint open sets in X of cardinality $c(X)$ (i.e. "sup = max").

THEOREM

If S is a closed base for the infinite T_2-space X *and S contains all finite subsets of* X, *then*

$$c(X) \leq c(\lambda_S X) = \sup\{c(\lambda_n S) \mid n\in\mathbb{N}\} = \sup\{c(X^n) \mid n\in\mathbb{N}\} =$$

$$= c(\Pi\{X \mid n\in\mathbb{N}\}).$$

PROOF

Put $c_1 = c(\lambda_S X)$, $c_2 = \sup\{c(\lambda_n S) \mid n\in\mathbb{N}\}$, $c_3 = \sup\{c(X^n) \mid n\in\mathbb{N}\}$ and $c_4 = c(\Pi\{X \mid n\in N\})$. It is known that $c_3 = c_4$, cf. [11] p.53.

$\underline{c \leq c_1}$. If A is a family of pairwise disjoint, open sets in X, then we may choose a non-empty basic open set $X\setminus S(A) \subset A$ for each $A \in A$ (i.e. $S(A) \in S$). Clearly $\{(X\setminus S(A))^+ \mid A\in A\}$ is a family of pairwise disjoint, open sets in $\lambda_S(X)$, of the same cardinality.

$\underline{c_1 \leq c_2}$. Let A be a family of pairwise disjoint open subsets of $\lambda_S(X)$, and card $A = \underline{m}$. Because each cardinal either is regular, or is a limit of regular cardinals (e.g. of successor cardinals), and because the case $\lambda_S(X) = \aleph_0$ is trivial, we may assume that $\underline{m}$ is an uncountable, regular cardinal. For each $A \in A$ we choose a finite number $S_{A1}, S_{A2}, \ldots, S_{An(A)} \in S$ such that

$$\emptyset \neq (X\setminus S_{A1})^+ \cap \ldots (X\setminus S_{An(A)})^+ \subset A.$$

Because $\underline{m}$ is uncountable and regular, we can find a natural number k such that the cardinality of $A^* =_{def} \{A\in A \mid n(A)=k\}$ is $\underline{m}$. Now

$$\{\lambda_k(S)\cap A \mid A\in A^*\}$$

is a family of cardinality $\underline{m}$ of pairwise disjoint, non-empty, open sets in $\lambda_k(S)$.

$\underline{c_2 \leq c_3}$. By II.7.5.b $\lambda_n(S)$ is the continuous image of a finite topological sum (one for each different type of n-mls) of copies of X^n. Obviously the Suslin number of this finite sum is the Suslin number of X^n, and the Suslin number of a continuous image of a space Y is $\leq c(Y)$.

$\underline{c_3 \leq c_2}$. X has at most c(X) many isolated points. If $c(X^k) = c(X)$ for all k, then trivially $c_3 \leq c_2$. However if $c(X^k) \geq \underline{m} > c(X)$ for some k, then there also is a disjoint, open family of card > $\underline{m}$ in the following open subset X^* of X^k, that is dense, except for isolated points:

$$X^* = \{(x_1,\ldots,x_k) \in X^k \mid \text{all } x_i \text{ are different}\}.$$

By methods analogous to the one in III.2.5 we can embed this set in $\lambda_l(S)$ for some l > k, and then construct a disjoint, open family of cardinality $> \underline{m}$ in this $\lambda_l(S)$. We omit the lengthy but elementary proof.

III.4. CONNECTEDNESS AND CONTRACTIBILITY

Two somewhat surprisingly nice properties of the superextension are shown in the results III.4.1 and III.4.3 of this section.

III.4.1. THEOREM

If X is a connected T_1-space and S is a closed subbase for X which contains all finite subsets of X, then $\lambda_S X$ is both connected and locally connected.

PROOF

We claim that for each finite number of arbitrary subsets $A_1,\ldots,A_n$ of X $A_1^+ \cap \ldots A_n^+$ is connected, which property suffices to prove the theorem.

If $M,N \in A_1^+ \cap \ldots A_n^+ \cap \lambda_m(S)$, then by III.2.7 there is a continuous image of X^{mm} in $A_1^+ \cap \ldots A_n^+$ which contains both M and N. So each two fmls's in $A_1^+ \cap \ldots A_n^+$ are in the same component of $A_1^+ \cap \ldots A_n^+$. By III.3.2 the fmls's in $A_1^+ \cap \ldots A_n^+$ are dense in this set, so $A_1^+ \cap \ldots A_n^+$ is connected.

COROLLARY

If X is a connected T_1-space (necessarily $T_{3\frac{1}{2}}$) and S is a normal T_1-

subbase for X, *then* $\lambda_S X$ *is connected, locally connected, compact and Hausdorff.*

PROOF

By II.4.5 CORO 1 $\lambda_S(X)$ is a quotient of λX, so $\lambda_S(X)$ is connected and locally connected. Of course $\lambda_S(X)$ is (super) compact (II.2.3) and Hausdorff (II.3.2).

III.4.2. THEOREM

The superextension λX *of* X *contains isolated points iff* X *does so.*

REMARK

There exists a (weakly normal) T_1-subbase S for the interval $[0,1]$, such that $\lambda_S[0,1]$ is the union of $i[0,1]$ and one isolated point. See V.2.1.

The above theorem is an immediate consequence of the following lemma:

LEMMA

An mls $M \in \lambda X$ *is an isolated point in* λX *iff* M *has a (minimal) defining set of finitely many isolated points in* X.

PROOF

If-part. M_{MIN} consists of finitely many, open-and-closed subsets of X. Hence

$$\cap\{O^+ \mid O \in M_{MIN}\}$$

is a basic open neighbourhood of M, which obviously contains no other mls's.

Only-if-part. If $M \in \lambda X$ is an isolated point, then $M \in \lambda_f X$, because $\lambda_f X$ is dense in λX (III.3.1). Let M be the minimal defining set of M, i.e. $M = \cup M_{MIN}$. Suppose $p \in M$ is not an isolated point in X, then we will derive a contradiction, by showing that any basic open neighbourhood $O_1^+ \cap \dots O_n^+$ of M, contains mls's, different from M. Indeed choose $p_{ji}=p_{ij} \in O_i \cap O_j \cap M \setminus \{p\}$ for $i,j = 1,\dots,n$. Then $\{\{p_{ij} \mid i\} \mid j\}$ is a linked system, and (by I.2.6) this system is contained in some fmls M', which is defined on $\{p_{ij} \mid i,j\}$. Obviously $M' \in O_1^+ \cap \dots O_n^+ \setminus \{M\}$.

III.4.3. LEMMA

Let X *be a* T_1*-space for which there exists a continuous surjective function* $f: X \to [0,1]$ *such that*

(i) f *is both open and closed*

(ii) $f^{-1}(0)$ *consists of a single point* p.

Then λX *is contractible to the point* i(p), *even in such a way that* i(p) *remains fixed. Moreover* X *is connected and pseudocompact, and* λX *is connected and locally connected.*

As a simple consequence there is the following

THEOREM

The superextension λX *of a* T_1*-space* X *is contractible in each of the following cases:*

(a) X *is the suspension* S(Y) *or cone* C(Y) *of a countably compact* T_1*-space* Y,

(b) X *is a finite, connected polyhedron,*

(c) X *is contractible, compact and Hausdorff.*

PROOF OF THE THEOREM

(a) If $X = S(Y) = [0,1] \times Y/\{0\} \times Y, \{1\} \times Y$ or $X = C(Y) = [0,1] \times Y/ /\{0\} \times Y$ and Y is a countably compact T_1-space, then X and the 'projection on [0,1]' (the first coordinate) satisfy the condition imposed on X and f in the lemma.

(b) Let X_0 and X_1 be the 0- and the 1-skeleton of the finite polyhedron X. By means of induction on the number of points in X_0, it is not hard to see that we can define a map $f: X_0 \to [0,1]$ which satisfies:

(i) $f^{-1}(0)$ is a singleton

(ii) If $p \in X_0$ and $f(p) \in (0,1)$ then $\exists p',p'' \in X_0$ such that ($f(p') < f(p) < f(p'')$ and the intervals pp' and pp'' are simplices of X_1).

(iii) If $p,p' \in X_0$ and $f(p) = f(p')$ then the interval pp' is not a simplex of X_1.

If $\bar{f}: X \to [0,1]$ is the simplex-wise-linear extension of the map f over X, then $\bar{f}$ satisfies the requirements from the lemma.

(c) is an immediate consequence of II.4.7.

PROOF OF THE LEMMA

First we show that X is connected and pseudo-compact, and λX is connected and locally connected. Let $f: X \to [0,1]$ be as required in the lemma: continuous, onto, open, closed and $f^{-1}(0)$ consisting of precisely one point.

If A is a proper, open-and-closed subset of X, then f(A) and $f(X\backslash A)$ are non-empty, open-and-closed subsets of [0,1]. I.e. $f(A) = f(X\backslash A) = [0,1]$, contradicting '$f^{-1}(0)$ is a singleton'.

If $g: X \to \mathbb{R}$ is a continuous surjection, then for some closed discrete $D \subset X$, $gD = \mathbb{N}$. Because f is a closed map, $fg^{-1}\mathbb{N}$ must be finite. We may suppose that $fg^{-1}\mathbb{N} = \{t\}$ is a singleton (and $t>0$). Now for each $n \in \mathbb{N}$ $fg^{-1}(n-1/4,n+1/4)$ is an open neighbourhood of t in [0,1]. So we may choose, successively, $p_n \in X$ such that

$$p_n \in g^{-1}(n-1/4,n+1/4),$$

$$f(p_{n-1}) < f(p_n) < t,$$

and

$$t - 1/n < f(p_n) < t.$$

Then $g\{p_n \mid n\in\mathbb{N}\}$ is a closed discrete subset of R, so $\{p_n \mid n\in\mathbb{N}\}$ is closed in X. However $f\{p_n \mid n\in\mathbb{N}\}$ converges to t, in contradiction to the assumption 'f is closed' (cf. V.2.3).

Because X is connected λX is connected and locally connected (see III.4.1).

Finally we come to the contractibility of X. A continuous $H: \lambda X \times [0,1] \to \lambda X$ will be constructed such that

$$H \mid \lambda X \times \{1\} = id_{\lambda X}$$

$$H(\lambda X \times \{0\}) = \{i(p)\}$$

$$H(\{p\}\times I) = \{i(p)\}.$$

Let $M \in \lambda X$, $t \in I$. We first define a family h(M,t) of closed subsets of X, by "modifying" the sets of M so, that some sets will be contained in $f^{-1}[0,t]$. Then we claim that h(M,t) is a pre-mls and we define H by

$$H(M,t) = \underline{h(M,t)}.$$

We define h(M,t) as the union of three families:

(α) $h(M,t) = \{S\in M \mid S\subset f^{-1}[0,t]\} \cup$

(β) $\cup\ \{S\cup\{x\} \mid S\in M,\ x\in f^{-1}(t)\} \cup$

(γ) $\cup\ \{S\cap f^{-1}[0,t]\cup f^{-1}t \mid S\in M\}$.

In order to complete the proof we have to check:

A. $h(M,t)$ is linked, which is trivial.

B. $h(M,t)$ is a pre-mls. We will show that if $G \subset X$ is closed and G meets all members of $h(M,t)$, then G contains a member of $h(M,t)$.

C. H is continuous, i.e. for every non-empty closed subset G of X $H^{-1}(G^+)$ is a closed subset of $\lambda X \times [0,1]$.

D. $H(M,1) = M$, $H(M,0) = i(p)$ and $H(i(p),t) = i(p)$. These are simple: the first equation follows from (α) and $f^{-1}[0,1] = X$, so that $\forall S \in M$ $S \in h(M,t) \subset H(M,t)$. The second follows from (γ): $H(M,0) \in (f^{-1}[0,0])^+ = \{p\}^+ = \{i(p)\}$. The third follows from (α): $\{p\} \subset f^{-1}[0,t]$ implies $\{p\} \in h(i(p),t) \subset H(i(p),t)$.

PROOF OF B.

We distinguish three cases.

1. $G \cap f^{-1}(t) = 0$. Hence $\forall S \in M$ $S\cap f^{-1}[0,t]\cap G \neq \emptyset$ (because of γ),

$f^{-1}[0,t]\cap G\in M$ (M is an mls),

$f^{-1}[0,t]\cap G\in h(M,t)$ (because of α).

2. $G \cap f^{-1}(t) \neq \emptyset$, but $f^{-1}(t) \not\subset G$. Choose $x \in f^{-1}(t)\setminus G$.

Now $\forall S \in M$ $(S\cup\{x\})\cap G \neq \emptyset$ (because of β),

i.e. $\forall S \in M$ $S\cap G \neq \emptyset$,

$G\in M$ (M is an mls),

$G\in h(M,t)$ (because of β).

3. $f^{-1}(t) \subset G$. Now $\forall S \in M$ $S\cap(G\cup f^{-1}[t,1]) \neq \emptyset$ (for if $S\cap f^{-1}[t,1] = \emptyset$, then $S\subset f^{-1}[0,t]$, so $S\in h(M,t)$ by (α), and thus $S\cap G \neq \emptyset$).

Hence $G\cup f^{-1}[t,1]\in M$ (M is an mls)

and $G\cap f^{-1}[0,t] = ((G\cup f^{-1}[t,1])\cap f^{-1}[0,t])\cup f^{-1}(t)\in h(M,t)$

(because of γ).

PROOF OF C

Let $G \in \mathcal{G}$. Now that we know that $h(M,t)$ is a pre-mls, it follows from (B.1) that if $G \cap f^{-1}(t) = \emptyset$, then

$$G \in \underline{h(M,t)} \quad \text{iff} \quad f^{-1}[0,t] \cap G \in M.$$

Similarly $G \cap f^{-1}(t) \neq \emptyset$, $f^{-1}(t) \not\subset G$ and (B.2) imply

$$G \in \underline{h(M,t)} \quad \text{iff} \quad G \in M.$$

Finally $f^{-1}(t) \subset G$ and (B.3) imply

$$G \in \underline{h(M,t)} \quad \text{iff} \quad G \cup f^{-1}[t,1] \in M.$$

Thus $H^{-1}(G^{+})$ is the union of the following three sets:

$$A_1 = \cup\{(G\cap f^{-1}[0,t])^{+}\times\{t\} \mid t\in[0,1]\}$$

$$A_2 = \cup\{\quad G^{+} \quad \times\{t\} \mid f^{-1}(t)\cap G\neq\emptyset\}$$

$$A_3 = \cup\{(G\cup f^{-1}[t,1])^{+}\times\{t\} \mid f^{-1}(t)\subset G\}.$$

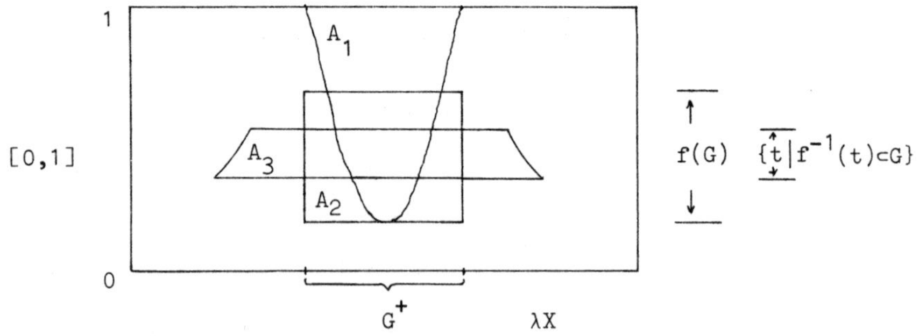

We will show that these three sets are closed (in $\lambda X\times[0,1]$):

$A_1 = A_1^{-}$: If $(N,t_0) \notin A_1$, then $\exists S \in N$

$$S \cap G \cap f^{-1}[0,t] = \emptyset.$$

If $t_0 = 1$, then $(X\backslash G)^{+} \times [0,1]$ is a neighbourhood of $[N,t_0]$ that is disjoint of A_1.

If $t_0 \neq 1$, then, since f is a closed map $\exists \varepsilon > 0$

$$S \cap G \cap f^{-1}[0,t_0+\varepsilon] = \emptyset.$$

Now

$$(X\backslash G \cap f^{-1}[0,t_0+\varepsilon])^+ \times (t_0-\varepsilon,t_0+\varepsilon)$$

is a neighbourhood of (N,t) that is disjoint of A_1.

$A_2 = A_2^-$: $A_2 = G^+ \times f(G)$ is closed because f is a closed map.

$A_3 = A_3^-$: If $(N,t_0) \notin A_3$ and $f^{-1}(t_0) \nsubseteq G$ then, since f is open, there is an $\varepsilon > 0$ such that

$$\lambda X \times (t_0-\varepsilon,t_0+\varepsilon)$$

is disjoint of A_3.
If $f^{-1}(t_0) \subseteq G$, then $\exists S \in N$

$$S \cap (G \cup f^{-1}[t_0,1]) = \emptyset.$$

Note that $t_0 \neq 0$. Because f is closed there is an $\varepsilon > 0$ such that

$$S \cap (G \cup f^{-1}[t_0-\varepsilon,1]) = \emptyset.$$

Now

$$(X\backslash(G \cup f^{-1}[t_0-\varepsilon,1]))^+ \times (t_0-\varepsilon,t_0+\varepsilon)$$

is a neighbourhood of (N,t_0) that is disjoint of A_3.

This completes the proof of lemma III.4.3.

CHAPTER IV THE SUPEREXTENSION RELATIVE ALL CLOSED SETS

Erst kommt das Fressen, dann kommt die Moral.

(Brecht)

In this chapter we specialize from the rather general point of view of the previous chapter. In the first place we restrict to "the superextension", i.e. the superextension of X relative G, the family of all closed sets.

In section 1 mainly the results of the previous chapter, applied to the superextension of general (of course at least T_1) spaces, are summarized. In the next section we specialize further, to λX for compact metrizable X and in particular for compact metric X. If X is metrizable, but not compact, then, by II.4.4, λX contains the Čech-Stone-compactification of X. So in this case λX is certainly not metrizable. If X is metrizable and compact, then λX is compact, Hausdorff and, by II.6.2, also has a countable weight. So λX is metrizable. For a compact metric space (X,d) an extension $\bar{d}$ of the metric d over λX is also explicitly given. The non-compact case is studied further in section 3. Particular attention is paid to two dense subsets, viz. $\lambda_f X$ = the set of all fmls, and $\lambda_{comp} X$ = the set of all mls's which have a compact defining set. Now $i(X) \subset \lambda_f X \subset \lambda_{comp} X$ and $i(X)$ is a closed subset of both. It is shown e.g. that $\lambda_f X$ and $\lambda_{comp} X$ always are metrizable, if X is so.

IV.1. THE SUPEREXTENSION λX OF X

IV.1.1.

Of course λX is a (super-) compact T_1-space in which X is canonically embedded. Trivially

(i) $\beta_G(X) =_{def} X^- = \omega(X)$,

the Wallman-compactification of X (cf. II.5.5), and X is C^*-embedded in λX (i.e. every continuous, bounded real-valued function on X has a continuous extension over λX, cf. II.4.1). In II.3.4 the following conditions were shown to be equivalent:

(ii) λX is Hausdorff

(iii) $\Longleftrightarrow$ $X^- = \beta_G(X)$ is Hausdorff

(iv) $\Longleftrightarrow$ $X^- = \beta X$, the Čech-Stone-compactification

(v) $\Longleftrightarrow$ X is normal

IV.1.2

By II.5.16 and III.1.2 we have that if (ii) - (v) hold, then

(vi) $\text{weight}(\lambda X) = \text{weight}(\beta X)$.

So as a consequence, if λX is metrizable then βX is metrizable, i.e. X must be compact and metrizable. On the other hand if X is compact and metrizable then λX is compact and Hausdorff and $\text{weight}(\lambda X) = \text{weight}(X) = \aleph_0$. So:

(vii) *λX is metrizable iff X is compact and metrizable.*

IV.1.3

In II.5 the following conditions on a closed T_1-subbase S for X were shown to imply

$$\lambda X \cong \lambda_S X.$$

In both cases the homeomorphism $\lambda X \to \lambda_S X$ is given by $M \to M \cap S$ for $M \in \lambda X$.

(i) S contains a subfamily S' which is a closed base and satisfies

$$(S'=)\ S'^{f\cap} \subset S \subset S'^{\cap} = G$$

and X is compact.

(ii) S normally screens G (then X must be normal).
Moreover it is shown that for every $S \in G$

(iii) $(iS)^- = S^+ \cap (iX)$

as is also easily seen from the equality $\beta_G(X) = \omega(X)$.

IV.1.4.

The weight, w, density, d, and cellularity number, c, were studied in III.1 and III.3. Let us recall the definitions:

$$w(Y) = \min\{\text{card } \mathcal{B} \mid \mathcal{B} \text{ is a (sub)basis for } Y\}$$

$$d(Y) = \min\{\text{card } D \mid D^- = Y\}$$

$$c(Y) = \min\{\text{card } \mathcal{A} \mid \text{each } A \in \mathcal{A} \text{ is open in } Y,\ \mathcal{A} \text{ is disjoint}\}.$$

The following equations (i) - (iv) are trivial consequences of III.1.2, III.3.5, III.3.8, II.5.16 and the following well-known inequality:

$$c(Y) \leq d(Y) \leq w(Y) \leq \exp d(Y) \qquad \text{if } Y \text{ is Hausdorff}$$

(Here for an infinite cardinal $\underline{m}$, $\exp \underline{m} =_{\text{def}} 2^{\underline{m}}$).

(i) If X is compact Hausdorff, then $w(\lambda X) = w(X)$

(ii) If X is normal, then $w(\lambda X) = w(\beta X) \leq \exp d(X)$

(iii) If X is Hausdorff, then $d(X) \geq c(\lambda X) = c(X \times X \times \ldots) \geq c(X)$

(iv) For any space X with topology $\mathcal{O}$:

$$c(X) \leq c(\lambda X) \leq d(X) = d(\lambda X) \leq w(X) \leq w(\lambda X) \leq \text{card } \mathcal{O} \leq \exp w(X).$$

IV.1.5

If X is not connected, $X = A \oplus B$, where $\oplus$ denotes the topological sum, then, by II.1.4.v, $\lambda X = A^+ \oplus B^+$. So III.4.1 shows in fact the first part of the following

THEOREM (cf. III.4.1)

(a) X *is connected iff* λX *is connected.*

(b) λX *is locally connected (and has* $\lambda(k)$ *many components) iff* X *has finitely many (viz.* k*) components.*

PROOF OF (b)

The only-if-part. If λX is locally connected then because it is compact, it contains only finitely many components, and only finitely many open-and-closed sets. However if $A \subset X$ is open-and-closed in X, then A^+ is open-and-closed in λX (cf. II.1.4.v). So X can contain only finitely many open-and-closed sets, and hence only finitely many components.

The if-part. Let $\pi: X \to \{1,\dots,k\}$ be the decomposition map. We will show that $\bar{\pi}: \lambda X \to \lambda\{1,\dots,k\} = \{1,\dots,\lambda(k)\}$ is the decomposition map of λX. Here $\bar{\pi}$ is defined as in II.4.5 or IV.1.20 by

$$\bar{\pi}(M) = \{S \in P\{1,\dots,\lambda(k)\} \mid \pi^{-1}S \in M\}.$$

($\{1,\dots,k\}$ and $\{1,\dots,\lambda(k)\}$ are throught of as discrete spaces). So we have to show that the point-inverses of $\bar{\pi}$ are open-and-closed and connected subsets of λX.

For each mls $K \in \lambda\{1,\dots,k\}$

$$\bar{\pi}^{-1}(K) = \cap\{(\pi^{-1}S)^+ \mid S \in K\}.$$

This non-empty subset of λX is open-and-closed in λX because each $\pi^{-1}S$ is open-and-closed in X and hence $(\pi^{-1}S)^+$ is open-and-closed in λX.

Next we show that $\bar{\pi}^{-1}(K) \cap \lambda_f X$ is connected, and hence also $\bar{\pi}^{-1}(K) = (\bar{\pi}^{-1}(K) \cap \lambda_f X)^-$ itself. Let $\{C_1,\dots,C_k\}$ be the family of components of X. Choose one point from each component: $p_i \in C_i$, $i = 1,\dots,k$ and put

$$P = \{p_1,\dots,p_k\}.$$

Then clearly $K' =_{def} \{P \cap \pi^{-1}S \mid S \in K\}$ is an pre-mls in λX of the same type as K. Let $M \in \bar{\pi}^{-1}K \cap \lambda_n X$ be arbitrary. We claim that there exists a continuous map

$$f': (C_1)^n \times \dots (C_k)^n \to \bar{\pi}^{-1}K$$

which contains both M and K in its (connected) image.

Construction of f'. We take for f' the restriction of the function f defined in III.2.7 for $M = M$, $M' = K'$, $A_i = C_i$, $i = 1,\dots,k$. We only have to specify what N we take in III.2.7. Let us repeat the argument of III.2.7. Suppose $M = \{x_1,\dots,x_n\}$ is the defining set of M. Let $\pi_M: \{(i,j) \mid$

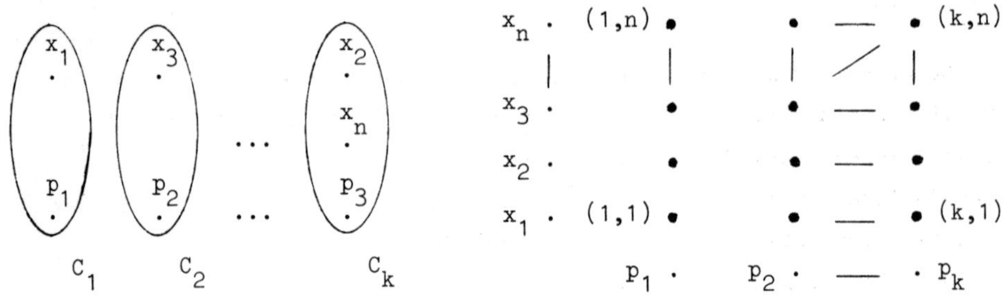

$| \ 1 \leq i \leq k,\ 1 \leq j \leq n\} \to \{x_1, \ldots, x_n\}$ be onto and such that

$$\pi_M\{(i,1), \ldots, (i,n)\} = M \cap C_i \qquad (i = 1, \ldots, k).$$

Let π_1 be 'the projection onto the first coordinate': $\pi_1(i,j) = p_i$. Let N be any mls in $P\{(i,j) \mid i,j\}$ containing all $\pi_1^{-1}S$, $S \in M$ and all $\pi_M^{-1}S$, $S \in K'$. Hence f_N: $(C_1)^n \times \ldots (C_k)^n \to \lambda_f X$ defined, as in III.2.2, by

$$f_N(((x_{ij})_{j=1}^n)_{i=1}^k) = \underline{\{\{x_{ij} \mid (i,j) \in S\} \mid S \in N\}}$$

satisfies

$$f_N((\pi_1(i,j))_{j=1}^n)_{i=1}^k) = M$$

and

$$f_N((\pi_M(i,j))_{j=1}^n)_{i=1}^k) = K'$$

and $\qquad f_N$ is continuous.

As in III.2.7 we define

$$f: (C_1)^n \times \ldots (C_k)^n \to \lambda_f(X)$$

by

$$f((x_{ij})_j)_i) = g(M, K', f_N(((x_{ij})_j)_i) =$$

$$= (M \cap K') \cup (M \cap f_N(((x_{ij})_j)_i) \cup$$

$$\cup (K' \cap f_N(((x_{ij})_j)_i)).$$

Then f satisfies our conditions and the proof that $\bar{\pi}^{-1}K$ is connected, is completed. From the above argument it can be seen that the following, more general lemma holds, which also implies that λX above is locally connected.

LEMMA

If X *has finitely many components,* $C_1, \ldots, C_k$, *and* T *is a subbase for* X *containing all finite subsets of* X, *and* $A_1,\dots,A_n \subset X$ *are subsets such that*

$$\{\{i \mid C_i \cap A_j \neq \emptyset,\ i \in \{1,\dots,k\}\} \mid j=1,\dots,n\}$$

is a pre-mls in $P\{1,\dots,k\}$, *then*

$$A_1^+ \cap \dots A_n^+$$

is connected (in $\lambda_T X$*).*

IV.1.6

Also in III.4 we showed that λX has (no) isolated points iff X has (no) isolated points. Because each 0-dimensional, compact, Hausdorff space of countable weight, without isolated points is (homeomorphic to) the Cantor-set, this observation completes the proof of

$$\lambda(\text{Cantorset}) = \text{Cantorset}$$

(by III.1.4, III.1.2, II.3.4 and III.4.2).

IV.1.7

Several sufficient conditions for contractibility of λX are given in III.4.3. Perhaps most remarkable is the fact that the superextension of the circle S^1 (and of the n-sphere, S^n) is contractible. Let us compare with the hyperspace $H(S^1)$ (for the definition, see III.2.8). Then the proof of contractibility of $H(S^1)$ is much simpler, than our proof of contractibility of λS^1. We may define e.g.

$$F: H(S^1) \times [0,1] \to H(S^1)$$

by
$$F(A,t) = \bar{U}_t(A) = \{x \in S^1 \mid d(x,A) \leq t.\text{diam } S^1\}.$$

As to the superextension of closed subspaces, products, and the extension of continuous functions we mention the following consequences of II.4.5 and II.4.7. These consequences often have simpler (sometimes trivial) proofs, than the corresponding results in II.4. Because anyway all deductions are very simple we omit the proofs.

IV.1.8. THEOREM (Cf. II.4.5. CORO 2 and II.4.7)

If Y *is a closed subspace of* X, *then* λY *is canonically embedded in* λX. *In fact each* M ∈ λY *is a pre-mls in* G *and* M → $\underline{M}$ *is an embedding.*

If Y *is a retract of* X, *and* X *is normal, with embedding* j: Y → X *and retraction* r: X → Y, *then* λY *is a retract of* λX. *The embedding and retraction can be defined by*

$$\bar{j}(M) = \underline{\{j(S) \mid S\in M\}} \qquad \text{(if } M\in\lambda Y)$$

and

$$\bar{r}(N) = \underline{\{S\subset Y \mid r^{-1}S\in N\}} \qquad \text{(if } N\in\lambda X).$$

IV.1.9. THEOREM (Cf. II.4.5. CORO 3)

If $\{X_i \mid i\in J\}$ *is a family of normal spaces,* $X = \Pi\{X_i \mid i\in J\}$ *and* $\pi_i\colon X \to X_i$ $(i\in J)$ *is the projection map, then*

$$g\colon \lambda X \to \Pi\{\lambda X_i \mid i\in J\}$$

defined by

$$g(M) = \underline{(\{S\in X_i \mid \pi_i^{-1}S\in M\})}_{i\in J}$$

is a continuous, closed, surjective "extension" of id_X.

IV.1.10. THEOREM (Cf. II.4.5)

(i) *If* f: X → Y *is continuous and* Y *is normal then*

$$\bar{f}\colon \lambda X \to \lambda Y$$

defined by

$$\bar{f}(M) = \underline{\{S\subset Y \mid f^{-1}S\in M\}}$$

is a continuous extension of f.
Moreoever $\bar{f}$ *is onto iff* f *is onto.*

(ii) *If* f: X → Y *is continuous and* Y *has a normal, binary,* T_1*-subbase* S *(e.g.* Y *is a product of compact linearly ordered spaces) then*

$$\bar{f}\colon \lambda X \to Y$$

defined by

$$\bar{f}(M) = \cap\{S\in S \mid f^{-1}S\in M\}$$

is a continuous extension of f.
(Observe that Y is necessarily compact Hausdorff).

IV.2. COMPACT METRIC SPACES

IV.2.1

In this section we assume that

$X = (M,d)$ *IS A COMPACT METRIC SPACE.*

Our main concern is the construction of a metric $\bar{d}$ on λM such that $i: (M,d) \hookrightarrow (\lambda M,\bar{d})$ is an isometry. We start with some definitions.

For $G \in G$ and $a \geq 0$ we denote the set of points which have distance $\leq a$ to G by

$$\bar{U}_a(G) = \{x\in M \mid \inf_{y\in G} d(x,y)\leq a\}.$$

(Observe the difference with $U_a(G)^-$, which is contained in, but need not be equal to $\bar{U}_a(G)$). The *Hausdorff metric* on G is denoted by d_H:

$$\forall S,T \in G \qquad d_H(S,T) = \inf\{a\in\mathbb{R} \mid T\subset\bar{U}_a(S) \text{ and } S\subset\bar{U}_a T\}.$$

(Observe that in this definition we may replace 'inf' by 'min'. Because $T \subset \bar{U}_a(S)$ and $S \subset \bar{U}_a(T)$ are not equivalent, neither can be omitted from the definition.)

For reference we state the trivial

IV.2.2. LEMMA

(a) $\forall G \in G \forall a \geq 0 \qquad d_H(G,\bar{U}_a(G)) \leq a$

(b) $\forall G \in G \forall a,b \geq 0 \qquad \bar{U}_b(\bar{U}_a(G)) \subset \bar{U}_{a+b}(G)$

(c) *If* $M,N \in \lambda M$ *then*

$$\forall S \in M \quad \bar{U}_a(S) \in N \iff$$
$$\iff \forall S \in M \forall T \in N \quad \bar{U}_a(S) \cap T \neq \emptyset \iff$$
$$\iff \forall S \in M \forall T \in N \exists x \in S \exists y \in T \quad d(x,y) \leq a.$$

REMARK

In (a) and (b) equality need not hold if there are no points in M precisely at a distance a of S. The merits of the equivalences in (c) is that the last formula is symmetric in M and N.

The promised metric d is introduced in

IV.2.3. LEMMA

If $M,N \in \lambda M$ *then the following set* A *of non-negative, real numbers*

$$A = \{a \mid a\in\mathbb{R},\ a\geq 0,\ \forall S\in M\quad \bar{U}_a(S)\in N,\ \forall T\in N\quad \bar{U}_a(T)\in M\}$$

has a minimum. This minimum is denoted by

$$\bar{d}(M,N) = \min A.$$

The following expressions for $\bar{d}$ *hold:*

(i) $\bar{d}(M,N) =_{def} \min\{a \mid a\in\mathbb{R},\ a\geq 0,\ \forall S\in M\quad \bar{U}_a(S)\in N,\ \forall T\in N\quad \bar{U}_a(T)\in M\}$

(ii) $\quad = \min\{a \mid a\in\mathbb{R},\ a\geq 0,\ \forall S\in M \forall T\in N \exists x\in S \exists y\in T\quad d(x,y)\leq a\}$

(iii) $\quad = \min\{a \mid a\in\mathbb{R},\ a\geq 0,\ \forall S\in M\quad \bar{U}_a(S)\in N\}.$

PROOF

Obviously if $a \in A$ and $a' \geq a$ then $a' \in A$. Now if $\underline{a} = \inf A$, then $\underline{a} + 1/n \in A$ for all natural numbers n; hence

$$\forall n \in \mathbb{N}\quad \bar{U}_{\underline{a}+1/n}(S) \in N.$$

Since M is compact it is easily seen that also $\bar{U}_{\underline{a}}(S) = \bigcap_{n\in N} \bar{U}_{\underline{a}+1/n}(S)$ meets all $T \in N$, and thus belongs to N. Similarly we find that $\bar{U}_{\underline{a}}(T) \in M$ for all $T \in N$. The equality of (i), (ii) and (iii) is trivial from the following consequence of IV.2.2.c:

If $a \in \mathbb{R}$, $a \geq 0$, then

$$\forall S \in M\quad \bar{U}_a(S) \in N \text{ and } \forall T \in N\quad \bar{U}_a(T) \in M \Longleftrightarrow$$

$$\Longleftrightarrow \forall S \in M\ \forall T \in N \exists x \in S \exists y \in T\quad d(x,y) \leq a \Longleftrightarrow$$

$$\Longleftrightarrow \forall S \in M\quad \bar{U}_a(S) \in N.$$

IV.2.4. THEOREM

If (M,d) *is a compact metric space, then the function* $\bar{d}$: $\lambda M \times \lambda M \to R$ *defined in IV.2.3 is a metric for* λM*, (compatible with the superextension topology).*
Moreover

(a) i: $(M,d) \to (\lambda M,\bar{d})$ is an isometry

(b) $\forall \mathcal{M},\mathcal{N} \in \lambda M \quad \bar{d}(\mathcal{M},\mathcal{N}) = \sup_{S\in\mathcal{M}} \min_{T\in\mathcal{N}} d_H(S,T)$

(c) *If we denote the open, resp. closed* ε*-neighbourhood of* $\mathcal{M}$ *in* λM*, by* $U_\varepsilon(\mathcal{M})$ *and* $\bar{U}_\varepsilon(\mathcal{M})$ *respectively, then*

(i) $\bar{U}_\varepsilon(\mathcal{M}) = \bigcap_{S\in\mathcal{M}} (\bar{U}_\varepsilon(S))^+$

(ii) $U_\varepsilon(\mathcal{M}) = \bigcup_{0<a<\varepsilon} \bigcap_{S\in\mathcal{M}} (\bar{U}_a(S))^+$.

We immediately obtain the following corollary of this theorem and II.4.4 CORO 1 (which stated that if $\mathcal{S}$ is normal, then $\lambda_{\mathcal{S}}M$ is a Hausdorff quotient of λM):

COROLLARY

If $\mathcal{S}$ *is a normal subbase for the compact metrizable space* M*, then also* $\lambda_{\mathcal{S}}M$ *is metrizable.*

PROOF OF THE THEOREM

It is trivial that $\bar{d}(\mathcal{M},\mathcal{N}) = 0 \iff \mathcal{M} = \mathcal{N}$ and that $\bar{d}(\mathcal{M},\mathcal{N}) = \bar{d}(\mathcal{N},\mathcal{M})$, while the triangle-inequality for $\bar{d}$ follows immediately from IV.2.2.b. In order to show that $\bar{d}$ is compatible with the topology of λM we only have to check that the (Hausdorff) $\bar{d}$-topology is coarser than the (compact) superextension topology. So let $\mathcal{M} \in \lambda X$ and let ε be a positive real number. Let $p_1,\ldots,p_n$ be an $\varepsilon/3$-net of M (i.e. $\forall x\in M \exists i \quad d(x,p_i)<\varepsilon/3$), and denote by $\mathcal{A}$ that (finite) collection of open sets, that are a union of some $U_{\varepsilon/3}(p_i)$'s. Now O is the open set of λM defined by

$$O = \cap\{A^+ \mid A\in\mathcal{A} \text{ and } \mathcal{M}\in A^+\}.$$

Clearly O is an open neighbourhood of $\mathcal{M}$ in the superextension topology and we claim that $O \subset U_\varepsilon(M)$. Indeed,

$$\forall S \in M\ \exists A \in A \quad S \subset A \subset \bar{U}_{2\varepsilon/3}(S)$$

and hence

$$O \subset A^+ \subset (\bar{U}_{2\varepsilon/3}(S))^+.$$

Using IV.2.3.iii we see that every mls $N \in O$ has a distance $\leq 2/3\varepsilon$ to M.

PROOF OF (a)

Let $p,q \in M$, $i(p) = \{S \mid p\in S\in G\}$, $i(q) = \{T \mid q\in T\in G\}$,

$$\bar{d}(i(p),i(q)) = \min\{a\geq 0 \mid \forall S \quad p\in S\in G \Longrightarrow q\in\bar{U}_a(S)\} =$$

$$= \min\{a\geq 0 \mid \quad q\in\bar{U}_a(\{p\})\} = d(p,q)\}.$$

PROOF OF (b)

First we show that

(*) $$\forall S \in S\ \forall N \in \lambda M \inf_{T\in N} d_H(S,T) = \min\{a\geq 0 \mid \bar{U}_a(S)\in N\}.$$

For suppose $\underline{a} = \inf_{T\in N} d_H(S,T)$. I.e. $\forall n \in \mathbb{N}\ \exists T \in N \quad T \subset \bar{U}_{a+1/n}(S)$ and $S \subset \bar{U}_{a+1/n}(T)$. Then certainly $\forall n \in \mathbb{N} \quad \bar{U}_{a+1/n}(S) \in N$, and hence $\bar{U}_a(S) \in N$, because M (and S) are compact. However if $\bar{U}_b(S) \in N$ for some $b \geq 0$, then

$$\inf_{T\in N} d_H(S,T) \leq d_H(S,\bar{U}_b(S)) \leq b$$

which proves *. Now (b) is an immediate consequence of IV.2.3.iii.

PROOF OF (c).

(i) The following equivalences hold:

$$\bar{d}(M,N) = a \leq \varepsilon \Longleftrightarrow \qquad \text{(by III.2.3.iii)}$$

$$\Longleftrightarrow \forall S \in M \quad \bar{U}_a(S) \in N \Longleftrightarrow$$

$$\Longleftrightarrow \qquad N \in \bigcap_{S\in M} (\bar{U}_a(S))^+.$$

(ii) follows from (i):

$$U_\varepsilon(M) = \bigcup_{0<a<\varepsilon} \bar{U}_a(M).$$

REMARKS

In (b) the 'sup' need not be a 'max', see V.2.2.b. In c(ii) the following modification is correct:

$$\text{c(ii)'} \qquad U_\varepsilon(M) \subset \bigcap_{S\in M} (U_\varepsilon(S))^+ \subset U_\varepsilon(M)^- \subset \bar{U}_\varepsilon(M).$$

However, all inclusion can be proper inclusions. In particular an $N \in \cap\{U_\varepsilon(S)^+ \mid S\in M\}$ for which in (b) the 'sup' is not attained, satisfies

$$N \notin U_\varepsilon(M).$$

Let us give the proofs. If $N \in U_\varepsilon(M)$, then $d(M,N) =_{def} a < \varepsilon$. Hence $N \ni \bar{U}_a(S) \subset U_\varepsilon(S)$, i.e. $N \in U_\varepsilon(S)^+$ for every $S \in M$, proving the first inclusion in c(ii)'. If $N \in \cap\{U_\varepsilon(S)^+ \mid S\in M\}$ and $O_1,\dots,O_n \in \mathcal{O}$, $N \in O_1^+ \cap \dots O_n^+$ then we have to show that

$$U_\varepsilon(M) \cap O_1^+ \cap \dots O_n^+ \neq \emptyset.$$

Choose $S_1,\dots,S_n \in N$ such that $S_i \subset O_i$, $i = 1,\dots,n$. We claim that for some $a < \varepsilon$

$$(**) \qquad \bar{U}_a(S_i) \in M \qquad \text{for all } i = 1,\dots,n.$$

First keep i fixed and suppose $\bar{U}_a(S_i) \notin M$ for all $a < \varepsilon$. Then $M \notin (U_\varepsilon(s_i))^+$, because each $T \in M$ is compact. Hence $\exists T \in M \quad T \cap U_\varepsilon(S_i) = \emptyset$ or equivalently $U_\varepsilon(T) \cap S_i = \emptyset$, contradictory to $S_i \in N \in U_\varepsilon(T)^+$. This proves $**$. Now we see that $\{\bar{U}_a(S) \mid S\in M\} \cup \{S_1,\dots,S_n\}$ is linked. Let K by an mls containing this family, then obviously

$$K \in \bigcap_{S\in M} (\bar{U}_a(S))^+$$

and hence $d(K,M) \leq a < \varepsilon$, and

$$K \in S_1^+ \cap \dots S_n^+ \subset O_1^+ \cap \dots O_n^+.$$

The third inclusion in c(ii)' is trivial. Finally let $N \in \cap\{U_\varepsilon(S)^+ \mid S\in M\}$. Then the following equivalences hold:

$$N \notin U_\varepsilon(M) \iff d(M,N) \geq \varepsilon \iff \qquad \text{(by III.2.3.iii)}$$

$$\iff \forall a < \varepsilon\ \exists S \in M \quad \bar{U}_a(S) \notin N \iff$$

$$\iff \forall a < \varepsilon \ \sup_{S \in M} \min\{a' \mid \bar{U}_{a'}(S) \in N\} \geq a \iff \qquad \text{(by * above)}$$

$$\iff \sup_{S \in M} \inf_{T \in N} d_H(S,T) \geq \varepsilon.$$

However for each separate $S \in M$, $N \in U_\varepsilon(S)^+$. Hence $\exists T \in N \quad T \subset U_\varepsilon(S)$. But then $\exists a < \varepsilon \quad T \subset \bar{U}_a(S)$, because T is compact, i.e. $\inf_{T \in N} d_H(S,T) \leq a < \varepsilon$. So the 'sup' cannot be attained.

IV.2.5. THEOREM

If X *is a compact metrizable space then* λX *is either 0-dimensional (if* λX *is 0-dimensional) or strongly infinite dimensional.*

REMARK

Observe that this theorem is not an immediate consequence of III.1.4.c. This theorem e.g. also applies to X = pseudo arc.

PROOF

If all components of X are singletons, then because X is compact Hausdorff, X is 0-dimensional, and by III.1.4 λX also is 0-dimensional. If, on the other hand C is a non-trivial component of X, then by IV.1.8 $\lambda C \subset \lambda X$. So we only have to show that λC is strongly infinite dimensional. We will do this by showing that λC contains an infinite product of non-degenerate continua. By a result of Lifanov, see [13], this is sufficient.

Choose $p_0, p_1, p_2, \ldots$ converging to p, all in C, and choose non-degenerate, disjoint continua $C_k \subset C \backslash \{p, p_0, p_1, p_2, \ldots\}$ for $k = -1, -2, -3, \ldots$. Choose $p_k \in C_k$ for $k < 0$. We define an mls M on $\{p, p_0, p_{\pm 1}, p_{\pm 2}, \ldots\}$ of the same type as M_1 in I.1.8.c.v. First we put

$$M_k = \{p_{-k}, p_0, p_1, p_2, \ldots, p_{k-1}\} \quad \text{for } k > 0,$$

$$M_k = \{p_k, p_{k+1}, \ldots, p_{-2}, p_{-1}, p_{-k}\} \quad \text{for } k < 0,$$

and

$$M_0 = \{p_0, p_1, p_2, \ldots, p\}.$$

Then $\{M_k \mid k=0,\pm1,\ldots\}$ is a pre-mls (see I.1.8.c) and we put

$$\underline{\mathcal{M} = \{M_k \mid k=0,\pm1,\ldots\}}.$$

Next we define a map, which will turn out to be an embedding,

$$f_{\mathcal{M}}: \prod_{k<0} C_k \to \lambda X$$

similar to the map in III.2.2. If $(x_k)_{k<0} \in \Pi\{C_k \mid k<0\}$ then let $f_{\mathcal{M}}((x_k)_k) = \underline{\mathcal{M}'}$, where

$$\mathcal{M}' = \{\{x_k \mid p_k \in S,\ k<0\} \cup \{p_k \mid p_k \in S,\ k\geq 0\} \mid S \in \mathcal{M}_{MIN}\}$$

is a pre-mls. Because $\mathcal{M}$ is minimally defined on $\{p_k \mid k\}$ and the C_k are disjoint, f is 1-1. So it only remains to show that $f_{\mathcal{M}}$ is continuous. Let O^+ be a subbasic open set in λX (i.e. $O \in \mathcal{O}$), and $f((x_k)_k) \in O^+$. Then either there is a finite set $J \subset \mathbb{Z}$ such that

$$f_{\mathcal{M}}((x_k)_k) \ni \{x_k \mid k<0,\ k\in J\} \cup \{p_k \mid k\geq 0,\ k\in J\} \subset O$$

or

$$f_{\mathcal{M}}((x_k)_k) \ni \{p_k \mid k\geq 0\} \cup \{p\} \subset O.$$

(This is so because each $S \in \mathcal{M}$ contains one of the M_k (see I.1.8.c), while M_0 is the only infinite M_k). In the latter case obviously

$$f_{\mathcal{M}}(\Pi\{C_k \mid k<0\}) \subset O^+.$$

In the first case, that J is finite, it is easy to see that

$$\cap\{\pi_i^{-1}(O\cap C_i) \mid i\in J,\ i<0\}$$

(where $\pi_i : \Pi C_j \to C_i$ is the projectionmap) is an open neighbourhood of $(x_k)_k$ that is mapped by $f_{\mathcal{M}}$ into O^+.

A simple combination of IV.1.1.vii, IV.1.5, IV.2.5 and IV 4.3 yields the following theorem

IV.2.6. THEOREM

The superextension λM *is a strongly infinite dimensional Peano-continuum (i.e. compact, metrizable, connected and locally connected) if and only if* M *is a metrizable continuum.*

Moreover in this case λM *is contractible if* M *satisfies one of the following conditions:*

(i) M *itself is contractible*

(ii) M *is a finite polyhedron*

(iii) M *is the suspension of a (compact, metrizable) space*

(iv) $\exists f: M \to [0,1]$, f *is open and continuous and* $f^{-1}(0)$ *consists of one point.*

IV.2.7.

It is known that a metrizable space X is strongly 0-dimensional iff it admits some non-archimedean metric d, (i.e. $\forall x,y,z \in X \quad d(x,z) \leq \max\{d(x,y),d(y,z)\}$) (cf. [5]). Moreover for a compact T_1-space X being 0-dimensional and being strongly 0-dimensional is equivalent. Now the following theorem concerns the extension $\bar{d}$ of this non-archimedean metric d.

THEOREM

If d *is a non-archimedean metric for the compact, 0-dimensional metric space* M, *then the extended metric* $\bar{d}$ *on* λM, *defined in IV.2.3, also is non-archimedean.*

PROOF

For the non-archimedean metric d, and the closed neighbourhoods $\bar{U}_a$ defined in IV.2.1, $\forall a,b \in \mathbb{R}$, $\forall G \in \mathcal{G}$

$$\bar{U}_b(\bar{U}_a(G)) \subset \bar{U}_{\max\{a,b\}}(G).$$

So if $\mathcal{M},\mathcal{N},\mathcal{P} \in \lambda M$, $d(\mathcal{M},\mathcal{N}) = a$ and $d(\mathcal{N},\mathcal{P}) = b$, then $\forall S \in \mathcal{M} \quad \bar{U}_a(S) \in \mathcal{N}$ and $\bar{U}_b(\bar{U}_a(S)) \in \mathcal{P}$, so $\bar{U}_{\max\{a,b\}} \in \mathcal{P}$. Thus $d(\mathcal{M},\mathcal{P}) \leq \max\{a,b\}$.

IV.3. TWO SUBSPACES, $\lambda_f X$ AND $\lambda_{comp} X$, of λX

IV.3.1.

In this section

IF X *IS A METRIC SPACE, WITH METRIC* d, *THEN WE MAY WRITE* X = (M,d).

IV.3.2

If (M,d) is a not-compact, metric space then λM is not-metrizable, but contains some interesting dense metrizable subspaces. Because $M \cup \{p\}$ has no countable neighbourhoodbasis in p for any $p \in i(M)^- \setminus i(M) \cong \beta M \setminus M$, we must look at $\lambda M \setminus (i(M)^-)$, i.e. $i(M)$ will be closed in the mentioned subspaces. We define, for a T_1-space X:

$$\lambda_f(X) =_{def} \lambda_f(G) = \{\mathcal{M} \in \lambda X \mid \exists F \subset X \quad F \text{ is finite and } \mathcal{M} \text{ is defined on } F\}$$

$$\lambda_{comp}(X) =_{def} \{\mathcal{M} \in \lambda X \mid \exists C \in \mathcal{G} \quad C \text{ is compact and } \mathcal{M} \text{ is defined on } C\},$$

both sets endowed with the subspace-topology from $\lambda(X)$. It is most important to observe that if $\mathcal{M} \in \lambda_{comp}X$ is defined (not necessarily minimally!) on the compact set C, then $\forall S \in \mathcal{M} \quad S \cap C \in \mathcal{M}$ and $S \cap C$ is compact. Similar to I.1.9.d, let $\mathcal{M}'$ be any maximal centered subfamily of $\mathcal{M} \cap PC$, then $S' =_{def} \cap\mathcal{M}' \in \mathcal{M}$, and no proper subset of S' can belong to $\mathcal{M}$, so even $S' \in \mathcal{M}_{MIN}$. Consequently $\forall S \in \mathcal{M} \exists S' \subset S \cap C \quad S' \in \mathcal{M}_{MIN}$. This proves the not-completely-trivial part of the following

PROPOSITION

Let $\mathcal{M} \in \lambda X$. Then $\mathcal{M} \in \lambda_{comp}X$ if and only if

(i) $\forall S \in \mathcal{M} \exists S' \in \mathcal{M}_{MIN} \quad S' \subset S$

(ii) $(\cup \mathcal{M}_{MIN})^-$ *is compact (here* $^-$ *denotes the closure in* X*).*

In this section we often use this proposition without explicite reference.

Next we may as well embed $\lambda_f(X)$ and $\lambda_{comp}(X)$ in $\lambda_{\mathcal{S}}(X)$ and have the same subspace-topology as in λX, if $\mathcal{S}$ satisfies suitable conditions.

IV.3.3. PROPOSITION

Let $\mathcal{S} = \mathcal{S}^{f\cap}$ be a closed base for X, *and let $\mathcal{C}$ be the family of all compact, closed subsets.*

(i) *If $P_f X \subset \mathcal{S}$, then $\lambda_f X$ is canonically embedded in $\lambda_{\mathcal{S}}(X)$, onto $\lambda_f(\mathcal{S})$ by the map* $j\colon \mathcal{M} \mapsto \mathcal{M} \cap \mathcal{S}$.

(ii) *If even $P_f(X) \subset \mathcal{C} \subset \mathcal{S}$ then $\lambda_{comp}X$ also is canonically embedded in $\lambda_{\mathcal{S}}X$, onto $\{\mathcal{M} \in \lambda(\mathcal{S}) \mid \mathcal{M}$ is defined on some compact set$\}$, by the map* $j\colon \mathcal{M} \mapsto \mathcal{M} \cap \mathcal{S}$.

REMARKS

(i) In IV.1.3 several other conditions on the subbase S were given, under each of which all of $\lambda_S X$ is homeomorphic to λX. Under any of these conditions of course $\lambda_f X$ and $\lambda_{comp} X$ can be embedded in $\lambda_S X$. Again in each case the embedding is the map $M \mapsto M \cap S$.

(ii) The condition '$S = S^{(f)}$, and S is a base' cannot be omitted as the following example shows:

let $\qquad T = P_f\mathbb{N} \cup \{\mathbb{N}\backslash\{n\} \mid n\in\mathbb{N}\}$.

Then T is a closed T_1-base for the closed sets of the discrete space N. Now

$$\lambda_f(T) = \beta_T(X) = \lambda_T(X) \; (\neq i\mathbb{N}).$$

So $i(\mathbb{N})$ is dense in $\lambda_f(T)$. However $\lambda_f\mathbb{N}$ is discrete (cf. III.4. or IV.3.4.vii).

PROOF

For (i) let $D = P_f(X)$ and $X' = \lambda_f X$. For (ii) let $D = C$ and $X' = = \lambda_{comp} X$.

In either case $D \subset S$, and if $M \in X'$ then $M \cap D$ is a pre-mls for M in G (= all closed sets). Hence $M \cap D$ also is a pre-mls in S, and consequently $M \cap S \in \lambda(S)$.

If $S \in S$, then

$$j^{-1}(S^+) = \{M\in X' \mid M\cap S\in S^+\} = \{M\in X' \mid S\in M\}$$

is closed in X'. So j is continuous. Finally we show that j is open. Let $O \in O$, and $M \in O^+ \subset X'$. Then

$$\exists D \in D \subset S \quad M \ni D \subset O.$$

Because $S = S^{(f)}$ is a base and D is (finite or) compact

$$\exists S \in S \quad D \subset X\backslash S.$$

Now in $\lambda_S X$

$$j(M) = M \cap S \subset X' \cap (X\backslash S)^+ \subset j(O^+) \subset \lambda_S X.$$

All tools have been gathered to prove the following

IV.3.4. THEOREM

(i) *$\lambda_f X$ is not compact, unless X is finite.*

(ii) *$\lambda_{comp} X$ is compact iff X is compact. In that case $\lambda_{comp} X = \lambda X$.*

(iii) *If X is Hausdorff, then iX is closed both in $\lambda_f X$ and in $\lambda_{comp} X$. Furthermore we have:*

$$\lambda_n(G) \text{ for each } n \in \mathbb{N}, \text{ and } \{N \in \lambda_f X \mid \text{type } N \leq \text{type } M\}$$

for each $M \in \lambda_f X$ are closed both in $\lambda_f X$ and in $\lambda_{comp} X$. However $\lambda_f X$ is dense in $\lambda_{comp} X$.

(iv) *The density, d, weight, w, and Suslin number, c, (for def. see III.1.1, III.3.5 and III.3.8) satisfy*

$$d(X) = d(\lambda_f X) = d(\lambda_{comp} X),$$

$$w(X) = w(\lambda_f X),$$

and moreover, if X is Hausdorff:

$$w(X) = w(\lambda_f X) = w(\lambda_{comp} X)$$

and

$$c(X) \leq c(\lambda_f X) = c(\lambda_{comp} X) = c(\Pi\{X \mid n \in N\}).$$

(v) *If X is Hausdorff, then $\lambda_f X$ and $\lambda_{comp} X$ are Hausdorff.*

(vi) *If X is $T_{3\frac{1}{2}}$, then $\lambda_f X$ and $\lambda_{comp} X$ are $T_{3\frac{1}{2}}$.*

(vii) *If X is discrete and infinite, then $\lambda_f X = \lambda_{comp} X \cong X$.*

(viii) *If X is connected, then $\lambda_f X$ and $\lambda_{comp} X$ are connected and locally connected.*

(ix) *If X has finitely many components, then $\lambda_f X$ and (consequently) $\lambda_{comp} X$ have finitely many components. Thus X, $\lambda_f X$ and $\lambda_{comp} X$ are locally connected.*

(x) *If X is 0-dimensional, then $\lambda_f X$ and $\lambda_{comp} X$ are 0-dimensional.*

(xi) *If X is contractible and Hausdorff, then $\lambda_f X$ and $\lambda_{comp} X$ are contractible.*

(xii) *If f: $Y \to X$ is continuous and X is Hausdorff, then there is a canonical, continuous extension $f_c\colon \lambda_{comp} Y \to \lambda_{comp} X$. Even if f is onto, then f_c need not be onto, but $f_c|\lambda_f Y\colon \lambda_f Y \to \lambda_f X$ is onto. If f is onto and perfect, then f_c is onto. If f is 1-1, then f_c is 1-1.*

PROOF

(i) Suppose $\mathbb{Z} \subset X$ and $\{M_k \mid k\in\mathbb{Z}\} \subset P_f\mathbb{Z}$ is the linked family of finite sets defined in I.1.8.c. (Here $\mathbb{Z}$ need not be discrete). Then by III.3.1 the family $\{M_k^+ \cap \lambda_f X \mid k\in\mathbb{Z}\}$ is a centered family of $\lambda_f X$-closed sets with an empty intersection.

(ii) If X is compact, then $\lambda_{comp} X = \lambda X$ because each $M \in \lambda X$ is defined on the compact set X.
If X is not compact, then there is some free filter $\{G_\alpha \mid \alpha\in J\} \subset G$. By III.3.1 $\{G_\alpha^+ \cap \lambda_f X \mid \alpha\in J\}$ and hence also $\{G_\alpha^+ \cap \lambda_{comp} X \mid \alpha\in J\}$ have the finite intersection property. However we claim that $\cap\{G_\alpha^+ \cap \lambda_{comp} X \mid \alpha\in J\} = \emptyset$, i.e. for no $M \in \lambda_{comp} X$, $M \supset \{G_\alpha \mid \alpha\in J\}$. Suppose there existed such an M, which was defined on the compact set C. Then choose one $\beta \in J$. Now $G_\beta \cap C \in M$, so $G_\beta \cap C \cap G_\alpha \neq \emptyset$ for all $\alpha \in J$. But then the filter $\{G_\alpha \mid \alpha\in J\}$ cannot be free.

(iii) It suffices to show that for each $M \in \lambda_f X$ the set $A = \{N\in\lambda_f X \mid \text{type } N \leq \text{type } M\}$ is closed in $\lambda_{comp} X$, because $\lambda_n X$ is a finite union of these sets and $i(X) = \lambda_1(X)$.
So let $K \in \lambda_{comp} X$, type $K \nleq$ type M. If $K \in \lambda_f X$ then we have seen in III.2.5 CORO that $K \notin A^-$. If $K \in \lambda_{comp} X \backslash \lambda_f X$ and M is an m-mls, then we will show that $K \notin \lambda_m(X)^-$. Let K be the set on which K is minimally defined ($K = (\cup K_{MIN})^-$, cf. IV.3.2). Obviously K is infinite. Choose m+1 different points in K and let $O_1,\ldots,O_{m+1} \in \mathcal{O}$ be disjoint, open neighbourhoods of these points. By I.1.10.b we can find compact $C_1,\ldots,C_{m+1},D_1,\ldots,D_{m+1} \in K$ such that

$$C_i \cap D_i \subset O_i \qquad (i=1,\ldots,m+1).$$

Then we can choose open neighbourhoods $U_1,\ldots,U_{m+1},V_1,\ldots,V_{m+1}$

of $C_1,\ldots,D_{m+1}$ respectively such that

$$U_i \cap V_i \subset O_i.$$

Hence $K \in U_1^+ \cap \ldots U_{m+1}^+ \cap V_1^+ \cap \ldots V_{m+1}^+ \subset \lambda_{comp}X \backslash \lambda_m X$.
This last inclusion holds because no m-point set in U_1 can meet each of $V_1,\ldots,V_{m+1}$.

(iv) The only non-trivial part is $w(X) = w(\lambda_{comp}X)$. All other equations immediately follow from III.1.1, III.3.5 and III.3.8. Let $\mathcal{B}$ be an open base for X, card. $\mathcal{B} = w(X)$ and $\mathcal{B}$ is closed under the taking of finite unions. We claim that $\{\lambda_{comp}X \cap B^+ \mid B \in \mathcal{B}\}$ is an open subbase for $\lambda_{comp}X$. Indeed if $O \in \mathcal{O}$ and $O^+ \cap \lambda_{comp}X$ is a subbasic open set and $M \in O^+ \cap \lambda_{comp}X$, then $\exists C \in M$ C is compact and $C \subset O$. Hence $\exists B \in \mathcal{B}$ $C \subset B \subset O$, i.e.

$$M \in B^+ \subset O^+.$$

(v) If $M,N \in \lambda_{comp}X$, $M \neq N$ then $\exists C \in M \exists D \in N$ $C \cap D = \emptyset$ and C and D are compact. Hence $\exists U,V \in \mathcal{O}$ $C \subset U$, $D \subset V$ and $U \cap V = \emptyset$. Now U^+ and V^+ are disjoint neighbourhoods of M and N.

(vi) Consider $\lambda_Z X$ (where Z = the family of zerosets). By IV.3.3 $\lambda_f X$ and $\lambda_{comp}X$ can be embedded in $\lambda_Z X$, which is (compact and) Hausdorff, by II.3.2 and II.3.1.iii.

(vii) If X is discrete then obviously $\lambda_{comp}X = \lambda_f X$ and $\forall M \in \lambda_f X$ $\{S^+ \mid S \in M_{MIN}\}$ is an open neighbourhood of M in λX, consisting of only M. So $\lambda_f X$ is discrete. Because $d(\lambda_f X) = d(X)$, $\lambda_f X$ and X have the same cardinality, i.e. they are homeomorphic.

(viii) and (ix) follow from the proof of IV.1.5. In fact it is shown that λX is (locally) connected by showing that $\lambda_f X$ is so, and using $\lambda_f X^- = \lambda X$.

(x) follows from the observation, made in the proof of (iv) that if $\mathcal{B} = \mathcal{B}^{(f)}$ is an open (or a closed) base for X, then $\{\lambda_{comp}X \cap B^+ \mid B \in \mathcal{B}\}$ is an open (or closed respectively) subbase for $\lambda_{comp}X$. So take $\mathcal{B}$ = the family of open-and-closed subsets of X.

(xi) Let H: $X \to [0,1] \to X$ be a contraction. Define

$$H_c: \lambda_{comp}X \times [0,1] \to \lambda_{comp}X$$

by

$$H_c(M,t) = \{S \in G \mid H_t^{-1} S \in M\}.$$

Obviously $H_c(M,t)$ is linked. Assume that it is not maximally linked: $\exists T \in G \quad H_t^{-1}T \notin M$ but T meets all $S \in H_c(M,t)$. Then there exists a compact $C \in M$ such that $C \cap H_t^{-1}T = \emptyset$. Consequently $H_tC \cap T = \emptyset$, contradictory to $H_tC \in H_c(M,t)$ (observe that H_tC is a closed set).
Let us next prove continuity. If $H_c(M,t) \in O^+$, $O \in \mathcal{O}$, then there exists a compact $C \in M$, such that $H(C\times\{t\}) \subset O$. (Observe again that $H(C\times\{t\})$ is closed and thus belongs to $H_c(M,t)$). Then there exist $\varepsilon > 0$ and $U \in \mathcal{O}$ containing C such that

$$(M,t) \in U^+ \times (t-\varepsilon,t+\varepsilon) \subset H^{-1}O.$$

Finally observe that f_c maps $\lambda_f X \times [0,1]$ in $\lambda_f X$.

(xii) Define f_c, as H_c above, by

$$f_c(M) = \{S \in G \mid f^{-1}S \in M\}.$$

Similar to above, $f_c(M)$ is an mls in G. Continuity follows from

$$f_c^{-1}(S^+) = (f^{-1}S)^+.$$

Let $f\colon \mathbb{N} \to \{0,1,1/2,1/3,\dots\}$ be any surjection, and $M \in \lambda_{comp}\{0,1,1/2,1/3,\dots\} = \lambda\{0,1,1/2,1/3,\dots\}$ an mls, minimally defined on the whole set $\{0,1,1/2,1/3,\dots\}$. If $M' \in \lambda_{comp}\mathbb{N}$ is defined on a compact and hence finite set C, then $f_c(M')$ is defined on the finite set $f(C)$, hence $M \notin$ Image f_c.
If $f\colon Y \to X$ is perfect and $M \in \lambda_{comp}X$ is defined on a compact set C, then $f^{-1}C$ is compact again. Now we can extend $\{f^{-1}S \mid S \in M_{MIN}\}$ to an mls N in the family of closed subsets of C. Then N is a pre-mls in the family of all closed subsets of Y, and $\underline{N} \in \lambda_{comp}Y$, and $f_c\underline{N} = M$.
If f is 1-1, and $M,M' \in \lambda_{comp}(X)$, then $\exists S \in M$, $S' \in M' \quad S \cap S' = \emptyset$, S and S' compact. Now $fS \in fM$ and $fS' \in fM'$ and $fS \cap fS' = \emptyset$, so $fM \neq fM'$.

IV.3.5.

Let us recall that $\lambda_f X = \bigcup_n \lambda_n(G)$, that each $\lambda_n(G)$ is closed in $\lambda_f X$ and that $\lambda_n(G)$ is a continuous image of a finite topological sum of copies of

X^n (cf. III.2.5.b). Before we give some applications, we first take a closer look at $\lambda_n(G)$, the set of all k-mls for $k \leq n$. We have seen (in III.4.2) that $\lambda_n(G)$ contains isolated points iff X contains isolated points. Indeed $\lambda_f X$ was discrete iff X was discrete. However the following holds if X has no isolated points:

LEMMA

Let X have no isolated points. Then each basic open set $O_1^+ \cap \ldots O_n^+$ in λX contains k-mls's for arbitrary large k.
In other words: each $\lambda_n(G)$, $n \in \mathbb{N}$, is nowhere dense in $\lambda_f X$.

PROOF

Using III.3.2, first choose $M \in O_1^+ \cap \ldots O_n^+ \cap \lambda_f X$ and then $M' \in (O_1^+ \cap \ldots O_n^+ \setminus \{M\}) \cap \lambda_f X$. Let M and M' be defined on the finite set M and M'. Then, because X is infinite, we may choose $p_1, \ldots, p_{2k+1} \in X \setminus (M \cup M')$. Let N be the 2k+1-mls

$$N = \{S \in G \mid S \text{ contains at least } k+1 \text{ points of } \{p_1, \ldots, p_{2k+1}\}\}.$$

Finally put $K = (M \cap M') \cup (M \cap N) \cup (M' \cap N)$. Then $K \in \lambda_m X$ for some $m > k$ and $K \in O_1^+ \cap \ldots O_n^+$ (see III.2.6.v).

From the above remarks one easily deduces:

IV.3.6. THEOREM

(i) *$\lambda_f X$ is of the first Baire-category iff X has no isolated points*

(ii) *$\lambda_f X$ is σ-compact iff X is σ-compact*

(iii) *$\lambda_f X$ is Lindelöf if X^n is Lindelöf for all $n \in \mathbb{N}$.*

(iv) *If X is neither 0-dimensional, nor strongly infinite dimensional, then $\lambda_f X$ is infinite dimensional, but a countable union of 0-dimensional subspaces (this is usually called: countably dimensional).*

IV.3.7

Let $X = (M,d)$ be a metric space. We define $\bar{d}\colon \lambda_{comp} M \times \lambda_{comp} M \to \mathbb{R}$, just as $\bar{d}$ was defined in IV.2.1 - IV.2.4. However there it was assumed that

M is compact, while we are now particularly interested in a non-compact M (otherwise $\lambda_{comp}M = \lambda M$) and we (have to) restrict ourself to those mls's that are defined on a compact set. We recall the following definitions from IV.2 (strictly speaking we generalize them to all metric spaces, instead of only the compact ones):

$$\forall G \in \mathcal{G} \quad \forall a \in \mathbb{R} \qquad \bar{U}_a(G) = \{x \in M \mid \inf_{y \in G} d(x,y) \leq a\}$$

$$\forall \mathcal{M},\mathcal{N} \in \lambda_{comp}M \qquad \bar{d}(\mathcal{M},\mathcal{N}) = \inf\{a \mid a \in \mathbb{R},\ a \geq 0,\ \forall S \in \mathcal{M}\ \bar{U}_a(S) \in \mathcal{N},\ \forall T \in \mathcal{N}\ \bar{U}_a(T) \in \mathcal{M}\}.$$

The proof of the following remarks is omitted because it is both very simple and similar to the proofs of IV.2.2 and IV.2.3.

(a) $\forall G \in \mathcal{G} \quad \forall a,b \geq 0 \qquad \bar{U}_b(\bar{U}_a(G)) \subset \bar{U}_{a+b}(G)$

Let $\mathcal{M},\mathcal{N} \in \lambda_{comp}M$. Then the following equivalences hold:

(b) $\forall S \in \mathcal{M} \quad \bar{U}_a(S) \in \mathcal{N} \iff$

$\iff \forall S \in \mathcal{M}_{MIN} \quad \bar{U}_a(S) \in \mathcal{N} \iff$

$\iff \forall S \in \mathcal{M}_{MIN} \quad \forall T \in \mathcal{N} \quad \bar{U}_a(S) \cap T \neq \emptyset \iff$

$\iff \forall S \in \mathcal{M}_{MIN} \quad \forall T \in \mathcal{N} \quad \exists x \in S\ \exists y \in T \quad d(x,y) \leq a \iff$

$\iff \forall S \in \mathcal{M} \quad \forall T \in \mathcal{N}\ \exists x \in S\ \exists y \in T \quad d(x,y) \leq a.$

(Recall that each $S \in \mathcal{M}_{MIN}$ is compact. cf. IV.3.2.i,ii).

(c) Moreover the following sets are equal:

$$\{a \mid a \geq 0,\ \forall S \in \mathcal{M} \quad \bar{U}_a(S) \in \mathcal{N},\ \forall T \in \mathcal{N} \quad \bar{U}_a(T) \in \mathcal{M}\} =$$

$$= \{a \mid a \geq 0,\ \forall S \in \mathcal{M} \quad \bar{U}_a(S) \in \mathcal{N}\} =$$

$$= \{a \mid a \geq 0,\ \forall S \in \mathcal{M} \quad \forall T \in \mathcal{N}\ \exists x \in S\ \exists y \in T \quad d(x,y) \leq a\},$$

and these sets have a minimum, that, by defining equals $\bar{d}(\mathcal{M},\mathcal{N})$.

Now we are able to prove that $\bar{d}$ is a metric on $\lambda_{comp}M$:

IV.3.8. THEOREM

If (M,d) *is a metric space then* $\bar{d}$*, defined above, is a metric on* $\lambda_{comp}M$*, compatible with the topology of* $\lambda_{comp}M$*. Moreover the map* $i: M \to \lambda_{comp}M$ *is an isometry.*

Consequently $\lambda_{comp}X$ *and* $\lambda_f X$ *are metrizable iff* X *is metrizable.*

REMARKS

In V.2.5 we will illustrate that $\bar{d}$ in general is not a complete metric, unless X is compact or discrete. We do not know under what conditions $\lambda_{comp}X$ is topologically complete, or e.g. Cech-complete if X is not compact. Of course X itself as a closed subset, has to be topologically complete or Cech-complete respectively. Cf. V.3.8.

Analogously to IV.2.7 one can show that $\bar{d}$ is non-archimedean iff d is non-archimedean. Hence the strong 0-dimensionality of X, of $\lambda_f X$ and of $\lambda_{comp}X$ are equivalent.

PROOF

It is obvious that $\bar{d}$ is a metric, and that i is an isometry. Let us first prove that the metric topology induced by $\bar{d}$ is stronger than (= containing) the subspace topology. Let $O \in \mathcal{O}$ and $M \in \lambda_{comp}X \cap O^+$. Hence $\exists C \in M_{MIN}$ $C \subset O$ and C is compact, as all members of M_{MIN}. Choose $a > 0$ such that $\bar{U}_a(C) \subset O$, then $U_a(M) \subset O^+$, (where $U_a(M)$ is the a-neighbourhood of M in $\lambda_{comp}X$ relative $\bar{d}$).

Next we have to show that for $M \in \lambda_{comp}X$ and $a > 0$ we can find $O_1,\ldots,O_n \in \mathcal{O}$ such that

$$M \in O_1^+ \cap \ldots O_n^+ \cap \lambda_{comp}X \subset U_a(M).$$

Let M be defined on the compact set C and let $p_1,\ldots,p_k$ be a finite a/3-net of C. Let A' be the collection of open a/3-spheres in X with midpoints $p_1,\ldots,p_n$, and $A = A'^{(f)}$ is the collection of (finite) unions of members of A. Put

$$O = \cap\{A^+ \mid M \in A^+,\ A \in A\} \cap \lambda_{comp}X.$$

Obviously O is a neighbourhood of M and we claim that $O \subset U_a(M)$. Indeed if $N \in O$, then $\forall S \in M_{MIN}$ $\exists A \in A$ $M \in A^+$ and $A \subset U_a(S)$. Hence $\bar{U}_a(S) \in N$ for all $S \in M$, i.e. $\bar{d}(M,N) \leq a$.

IV.3.9

If X has no isolated points, then from IV.3.6 ($\lambda_f X$ is of the first Baire category) it follows that no point of $\lambda_f X$ has compact neighbourhoods. A similar result also holds for $\lambda_{comp}X$:

THEOREM

Let X be Hausdorff and not-compact. Then the interior of any compact subset of $\lambda_{comp}X$ *or* $\lambda_f X$ *either is empty or contains at most isolated points.*

PROOF

This has only to be proved for $\lambda_{comp}X$. Let $O_1,\dots,O_n \in \mathcal{O}$ and let $O_1^+ \cap \dots O_n^+ \cap \lambda_{comp}X$ be a non-empty basic open set in $\lambda_{comp}X$, containing no isolated points. We will show that this set has no compactification in $\lambda_{comp}X$. Choose two different $M,M' \in O_1^+ \cap \dots O_n^+ \cap \lambda_{comp}X$, and choose a free maximal centered system F of closed subsets of X. Observe that F is an mls (even $F \in \beta_G X \subset \lambda X\backslash\lambda_{comp}X$). Let

$$N = (M\cap M') \cup (M\cap F) \cup (M'\cap F) \in \lambda X.$$

Notice that $N \in O_1^+ \cap \dots O_n^+\backslash\lambda_{comp}X$. Now the following family of subsets of $O_1^+ \cap \dots O_n^+ \cap \lambda_{comp}X$ has the finite intersection property:

$$\{O_1^+\cap\dots O_n^+\cap\lambda_f X\cap S^+ \mid S\in N\}.$$

However, the only point in the intersection of the closures of these sets in λX is N, as is easily seen and $N \notin \lambda_{comp}X$.

IV.3.10

Recall that $\lambda X \subset \lambda Y$ for $X \subset Y$ only holds if X is a closed subset of Y. For λ_f and λ_{comp} a more general result is true:

THEOREM

If $X \subset Y$ *then there are natural embeddings* $j_f\colon \lambda_f X \subset \lambda_f Y \subset \lambda Y$ *and* $j_c\colon \lambda_{comp}X \subset \lambda_{comp}X \subset \lambda Y$ *given by the map* $M \longmapsto \underline{M}$. *Moreover if Y is normal, then*

$$(j_f\lambda_f X)^- = (j_c\lambda_{comp}X)^- = \{M\in\lambda Y \mid M \textit{ is defined on } X^-\}.$$

If $X^- \neq Y$, *then the interior of* $(j_f\lambda_f X)^-$ *contains at most isolated points.*

PROOF

It is easy to see that each $M \in \lambda_{comp}X$ is a pre-mls in Y. If G is a closed subset of Y, then $\underline{M} \in G^+$ iff $M \in (G \cap X)^+$. So the first part of the theorem is simple.

For the second part, observe first that $\lambda_f X$ is dense in $\lambda_{comp} X$, so $(j_f \lambda_f X)^- = (j_c \lambda_{comp} X)^-$. Moreover $X^* = \{M \in \lambda Y \mid M \text{ is defined on } X^-\}$ is closed: suppose $N \notin X^*$. Then $\exists S \in N \quad S \cap X^- \notin N$. Hence $\exists T \in N$ $S \cap T \subset Y \backslash X^-$. Because Y is normal, there are open neighbourhoods U of S and V of T such that $U \cap V \subset (Y \backslash X^-)$. Now $N \in U^+ \cap V^+ \subset \lambda Y \backslash X^*$. Also it is easily seen that $j_c \lambda_{comp} X \subset \{M \in \lambda Y \mid M \text{ is defined on } X\} \subset X^*$, so $(j_c \lambda_{comp} X)^- \subset X^{*-} = X^*$. Next we leave the proof that $j_f \lambda_f X$ is dense in X^* to the reader (cf. III.3.1 and III.3.3).

Finally if $O_1^+ \cap \ldots O_n^+$ is a basic open set in λY and the O_i are not finite, and $p \in Y \backslash \lambda X^-$, then we can choose $M, M' \in \lambda_f Y \cap O_1^+ \cap \ldots O_n^+$ and

$$N = (M \cap M') \cup (M \cap i_y(p)) \cup (M' \cap i_y(p)) \in O_1^+ \cap \ldots O_n^+ .$$

Choose disjoint $S \in M$, $T \in M'$ and observe that

$$N \in (S \cup \{p\})^+ \cap (T \cup \{p\})^+ \subset \lambda Y \backslash X .$$

This shows that under the mentioned conditions X^* is nowhere dense.

CHAPTER V EXAMPLES AND OPEN QUESTIONS

No problem is so big or so
complicated that it can't
be run away from

(Linus van Pelt)

This chapter starts with a description of the superextension of some simple spaces such as the natural and the real numbers, $\mathbb{N}$ and $\mathbb{R}$, the closed unit interval, $[0,1]$, the circle, S^1, the cantorset, C, a converging point-sequence, $\{0,1,1/2,1/3,\ldots\}$. The superextension of a finite (discrete) T_1-space has been treated extensively in I.3. Some other examples follow, that are meant to illustrate special properties of superextensions. E.g. the example of the superextension of a linearly ordered space with respect to the natural order-subbase, and the example of the sin 1/x -curve, where an indication is given why the superextension is (locally arcwise) connected.

In section 2 some (counter) examples are collected, that require more (ad hoc) construction than the rather theoretical smooth examples of the first section. E.g. four weakly normal subbases $\mathcal{S}_i$ for the closed interval $[0,1]$ are given such that $\lambda_{\mathcal{S}_i}[0,1]$ is a circle, is not locally connected, is $[0,1]$ union one isolated point and is not Hausdorff respectively. Also other counterexamples that have been promised in earlier chapters are presented.

Finally the third section presents a short discussion of the main unsolved questions on superextensions, and supercompactness, as seen by the author.

V.1. EXAMPLES

V.1.1. $\lambda\mathbb{N}$, THE SUPEREXTENSION OF THE NATURAL NUMBERS

$\lambda\mathbb{N}$ is compact (II.2.3), Hausdorff (II.3.4), 0-dimensional (III.1.4) and contains a countable, dense set of isolated points: $\lambda_f\mathbb{N} = \lambda_{comp}\mathbb{N}$ (III.3.3, IV.3.4.vii). The closure of $\mathbb{N}$ in $\lambda\mathbb{N}$ is $\beta\mathbb{N}$, its Čech-Stone compactification (II.3.4). But $\lambda\mathbb{N}$ is not homeomorphic to $\beta\mathbb{N}$, e.g. $\lambda\mathbb{N}$ contains the following converging point sequence:

If

$$M_n = \{S \mid S \supseteq \{2,\ldots,n\} \cup (1 \in S, S \cap \{2,\ldots,n\} \neq \emptyset\})\}$$

then for $n \to \infty$

$$M_n \to M = \{S \mid S=\mathbb{N} \text{ or } S=\{2,3,4,\ldots\} \text{ or } (1\in S, S\cap\{2,3,4,\ldots\}\neq\emptyset)\}.$$

Finally

$$\lambda\mathbb{N} \cong \lambda(\beta\mathbb{N})$$

(see II.5.17).

V.1.2. $\lambda\mathbb{R}$, THE SUPEREXTENSION OF THE REAL NUMBERS

$\lambda\mathbb{R}$ is compact (II.2.3), Hausdorff (II.3.4), connected and locally connected (III.4.1) and separable (III.3.5). The closure of $\mathbb{R}$ in $\lambda\mathbb{R}$ is $\beta\mathbb{R}$, its Čech-Stone-compactification, (II.3.4), and $\lambda\mathbb{R} = \lambda(\beta\mathbb{R})$ (see II.5.17). $\lambda\mathbb{R}$ 'inherits' from $\beta\mathbb{R}$ its contractibility (III.4.3.c), and its weight = card $\mathbb{R}$ (III.1.2). The subspace $\lambda_{comp}\mathbb{R}$ of $\lambda\mathbb{R}$ is dense, metrizable, contractible, separable, locally connected, (IV.3.4), strongly infinite dimensional (IV.3.10 & III.1.4.c), and in no point locally compact (IV.3.9). It is not known whether or not $\lambda_{comp}\mathbb{R}$ is topologically complete, i.e. is a G_δ in $\lambda\mathbb{R}$ (cf. V.3.8).

V.1.3. $\lambda[0,1]$ AND λS^1, THE SUPEREXTENSION OF A CLOSED INTERVAL, AND OF THE CIRCLE

$\lambda[0,1]$ and λS^1 are compact, metric, locally connected, contractible and strongly infinite dimensional (IV.2.6). See further V.3.1 and V.3.2.

V.1.4. λC, THE SUPEREXTENSION OF THE CANTOR MIDDLE-THIRD-SET C

λC is homeomorphic to C (cf. IV.1.6).

V.1.5. $\lambda\{0,1,1/2,1/3,\ldots\}$, THE SUPEREXTENSION OF A CONVERGING POINT-SEQUENCE

$\lambda\{0,1,1/2,1/3,\ldots\}$ is compact, metric, and zerodimensional (IV.2.6). The set of isolated points is $\lambda_f\{1,1/2,1/3,\ldots\}$, which of course is countable (III.4.2 LEMMA). Let us denote this set by N, and the set of non-isolated points by C. We will prove below that C is dense in itself. Because C is compact, metrizable and 0-dimensional this implies that C is homeomorphic to the Cantor middle-third-set. This characterizes

$\lambda\{0,1,1/2,1/3,\dots\}$ up to homeomorphisms. Indeed it is easy to proof that:

All compact, 0-dimensional, metrizable spaces, that are the union of a dense set of isolated points and a perfect set are homeomorphic.

Proof that C is perfect. If $M \in C$, define then

$$M_n = \{S \mid \text{either } (S \in M, S \subset \{1, \tfrac{1}{2}, \dots, \tfrac{1}{n}\}) \text{ or } (S \cup \{\tfrac{1}{n+1}, \tfrac{1}{n+2}, \dots, 0\} \in M, S \text{ contains at least two points of } 1/n+1,\ 1/n+2,\ 0)\}.$$

It is easily checked that M_n is a pre-mls, $\underline{M}_n \in C$, and $\underline{M}_n \to M$ for $n \to \infty$.

V.1.6. LINEARLY ORDERED SPACES

Let $(X,<)$ be a linearly ordered set and

$$S = \{\{x \in X \mid x<a\} \mid a \in X\} \cup \{x \in X \mid a<x\} \mid a \in X\}.$$

Then $\lambda_S X$ is homeomorphic (i.e. order-isomorphic) to the Dedekind completion of X. For details see [16].

V.1.7. COFINITE AND ANTI-HAUSDORFF SPACES

A *cofinite* or *Zariski space* is an infinite topological space in which the only open sets are: $\emptyset$ and the sets with a finite complement. They are examples of anti-Hausdorff spaces.

A topological space X (with $\mathcal{O}$ = the family of non-empty open sets) is called *anti-Hausdorff* if it satisfies any (and hence all) of the following equivalent properties:

(i) each two non-empty open sets meet
(ii) each non-empty open set is dense
(iii) each open set is connected
(iv) $\mathcal{O}$ is a centered family
(v) the open subbase $\{O^+ \mid O \in \mathcal{O}\}$ for λX is a centered family
(vi) the non-empty open sets in λX constitute a centered family
(vii) every two non-empty open sets in λX meet
(viii) X is dense in λX.

For (v) - (viii) it is assumed that X is T_1 and contains more than two points. The equivalences (i) $\Longleftrightarrow$ ... (vii) are obvious. The last condition, (viii), is most easily seen to be equivalent to (iv). In particular we have:

X is anti-Hausdorff iff λX is anti-Hausdorff, iff X is dense in λX.

If X is cofinite then λX is anti-Hausdorff and of the same weight (viz. card X). However λX is not cofinite: for a finite set $F \subset X$ of more then one point F^+ is an infinite proper closed subset of λX.

V.1.8. THE FIRST COUNTABILITY AXIOM

Let $X = X' \cup X''$ be the Alexandroff-double of the circle (i.e. X compact Hausdorff, $X' \cong$ circle, X'' = the set of, continuously many, isolated points of X, which is dense). Let I' be an arc in X' and I'' the corresponding set of points from X'', and choose $p \in X''\backslash I''$. We may define an mls $M \in \lambda X$ as follows:

$$M = \{S \in G \mid I' \cup I'' \subset S \text{ or } (p \in S \text{ and } (I' \cup I'') \cap S \neq \emptyset)\}$$

A neighbourhoodbasis of M is obtained by considering all sets

$$\{p,q_1\}^+ \cap \dots \{p,q_n\}^+ \cap (I' \cup I'')^+ \qquad n \in \mathbb{N},\ q_1,\dots,q_n \in I' \cup I''.$$

It is easily seen that M has no countable neighbourhoodbasis, i.e. λX does not satisfy the first axiom of countability, although X does satisfy this axiom and is compact and Hausdorff.

V.1.9. EXAMPLE ON CONNECTEDNESS

Let X be the sinus 1/x curve:

$X = \{0\} \times [-1,1] \cup$

$\cup \{(t, \sin 2\pi/t) \mid t \in (0,1]\}$.

Theorem IV.2.6 (cf. III.4.1) states that λX is a Peano-continuum. For illustration we will indicate an arc in λX that connects (0,0) and (1,0) in X. This can easily be changed e.g. to a proof that in every basic (!) neighbourhood 0^+ of (0,0) in λX every two points of X can be connected by an arc.

First we "pull a closed interval G_t our of (1,0)" (for $0<1-t<1/2$) until the projection of G_t on the Y-axis is long enough. Then, for

$1/2 < 1-t < 1$ we let both endpoints run to the left, in such a way, that the projection of G_t on the Y-axis always contains 0.

$$G_t = \begin{cases} \{(s,\sin 2\pi/s) \mid (1-t)\leq s\leq 1\} & \text{for } 1/2 \leq t \leq 1 \\ \{(s,\sin 2\pi/s) \mid t/(t+1)\leq s\leq t\} & \text{for } 0 < t \leq 1/2. \end{cases}$$

Finally put

$$M_t = \begin{cases} \overline{\{G_t\} \cup \{\{(0,0),x\} \mid x\in G_t\}} & \text{for } 0 < t \leq 1 \\ i((0,0)) & \text{for } t = 0. \end{cases}$$

Then $\{M_t \mid 0\leq t\leq 1\}$ is an arc in λX with endpoints $i((0,0))$ and $i((1,0))$.

V.2. CONSTRUCTIONS

V.2.1. SOME SUPEREXTENSIONS OF [0,1] RELATIVE SUBBASES

Let I be the family of all closed subintervals of [0,1]. Consider the following four closed T_1-subbases for [0,1]:

$$S_1 = I \cup \{\{0,1\}\}$$

$$S_2 = I \cup \{[0,1/n] \cup [1-1/n,1] \mid n\in\mathbb{N},\ n\geq 3\} \cup \{\{0,1\}\}$$

$$S_3 = \{[a,b]\in I \mid b-a\leq 1/2\} \cup \{\{0,1\}\}$$

$$S_4 = I \cup \{\{a,b\} \mid 0\leq a<b\leq 1\}.$$

All are easily seen to be weakly normal. We give no proofs, but only a description of the (free) mls's in S_i and of λ_{S_i}, i = 1,2,3,4. For more details see [9].

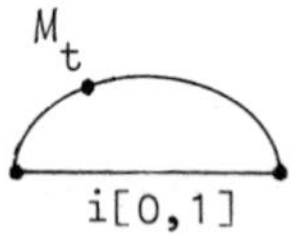

$\lambda_{S_1}[0,1] \cong S^1$.
The free mls's in S_1 are:

$$M_t = \overline{\{\{0,1\},[0,t],[t,1]} \qquad 0 < t < 1$$

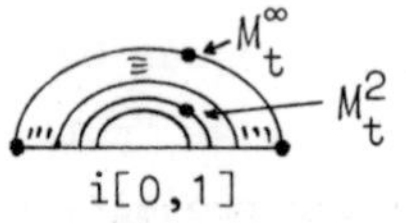

$\lambda_{S_2}[0,1]$ is homeomorphic to a sequence of half-circles converging to an outer-half circle union the diameter of this outer-half circle. Described analytically:

$$\lambda_{S_2} \cong [-1,1] \times \{0\} \cup \bigcup_{n\geq 3} \{(x,y) \mid x^2+y^2=(1-1/n)^2,\ y>0\} \cup$$

$$\cup \{(x,y) \mid x^2+y^2=1,\ y>0\}.$$

This space is not locally connected.

The free mls's in S_2 are:

$$M_t^n = \underline{\{[0,1/n] \cup [1-1/n,1],[1/n,t],[t,1-1/n]\}} \quad n > 3,\ 1/n<t<1-1/n$$

and

$$M_t^\infty = \underline{\{\{0,1\},[0,t],[t,1]\}} \qquad 0 < t < 1.$$

$\lambda_{S_3}[0,1]$ is homeomorph to $[0,1]$ union one isolated point. The only free mls in S_3 is $\{\{0,1\},[0,1/2],[1/2,1]\}$.

$\lambda_{S_4}[0,1]$ is not Hausdorff. There are three types of free mls's in S_4. For $0 \leq x < y \leq z < 1$ we define

$$M_{xyz} = \{S \in S_4 \mid S \text{ contains at least two points of } x,y,z\}$$

$$_xM_{yz} = \{S \in S_4 \mid S \text{ contains } [y,z] \text{ or } (x \in S \text{ and } S \cap [y,z] \neq \emptyset)\}$$

$$_{xy}M_z = \{S \in S_4 \mid S \text{ contains } [x,y] \text{ or } (z \in S \text{ and } S \cap [x,y] \neq \emptyset)\}.$$

One can show that e.g. $M_{0,1/4,1/2}$ and $M_{0,1/4,3/4}$ do not have disjoint basic open neighbourhoods in $\lambda_{S_4}[0,1]$.

V.2.2.

We turn again to example I.1.8.d:

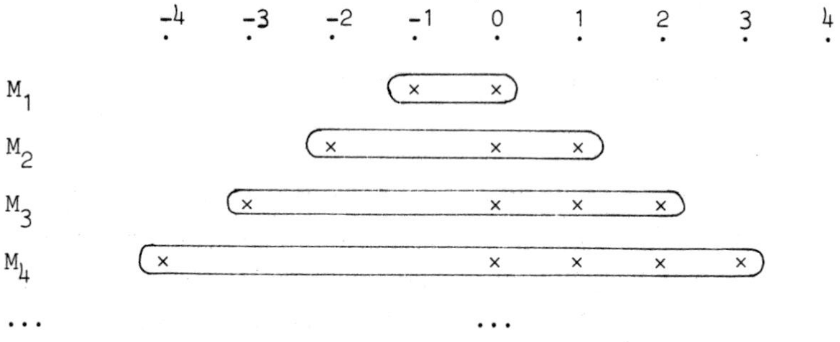

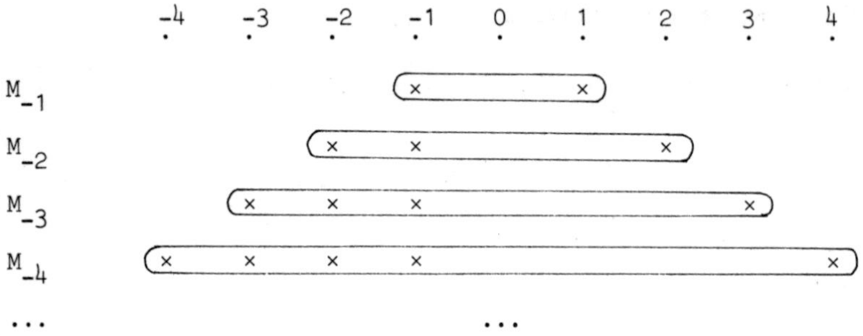

In formula:

$$M_k = \begin{cases} \{-k,0,1,2,\ldots,k-1\} & \text{for } k > 0, \text{ and} \\ \{k,k+1,\ldots,-2,-1,|k|\} & \text{for } k < 0. \end{cases}$$

It was proved in I.1.8.d that $\{M_k \mid k\}$ is a pre-mls in $P_f N$ and that $\{M_k \mid k\} \cup \{\{0,1,2,3,\ldots\}\}$ and $\{M_k \mid k\} \cup \{\{-1,-2,-3,\ldots\}\}$ are pre-mls's in $P\mathbb{N}$, and generate the only two mls's containing $\{M_k \mid k\}$.

Now consider $\lambda\mathbb{R}$.

(a) In the proof of III.4.1 it was shown that for any finite number of arbitrary subsets $A_1,\ldots,A_n \subset \mathbb{R}$ $A_1^+ \cap \ldots A_n^+$ is connected. The above example shows that this is not true for countable intersections: $\cap\{M_k^+ \mid k\} \subset \lambda\mathbb{R}$ consists of precisely two points.

(b) Let ϕ: $\mathbb{R} \to (0,1)$ be an orderpreserving homeomorphism (that I do not care to specify) and $M = [0,1]$. Let $\mathcal{M} \in \lambda M$ be the (only) mls containing $\{\phi M_k \mid k\} \cup \{(\phi\{0,1,2,3,\ldots\})^-\}$ as minimal sets. If d is the ordinary metric of M, and $\bar{d}$ the extension described in IV.3, then

$$\bar{d}(\mathcal{M},i(1)) = \sup_{S \in \mathcal{M}_{MIN}} \min d(S,1) = 1,$$

although $\min d(S,1) < 1$ for all $S \in \mathcal{M}$. So this sup is not a max (cf. IV.2.4.b).

(c) Recall that it is not known whether $\lambda_{comp}\mathbb{R}$ is topologically complete (see also V.2.4 and V.3.8). One may try to prove this by constructing a co-compact (sub)base for $\lambda_{comp}\mathbb{R}$, in the sense of [1]. But the following first try does not work. Let $\mathcal{C} = \{S \subset \mathbb{R} \mid S \text{ is compact}\}$. Then it is easy to see that $\{C^+ \mid C \in \mathcal{C}\}$ is a 'closed subbase' in the sense of [1], i.e. $\{int(C^+) \mid C\in\mathcal{C}\}$ is a subbase for the open sets. This subbase does not generate a compact co-space (by serving as a subbase for the closed sets of this "co-space", which thus has a weaker topology on the same underlying set). Indeed $\{M_k^+\cap\lambda_{comp}\mathbb{R} \mid k\}$ is a centered family, but it has an empty intersection, as we easily see e.g. as follows: if $\mathcal{M} \in \cap\{M_k^+\cap\lambda_{comp}\mathbb{R} \mid k\}$, then $\mathcal{M}$ is defined on some compact set (and on all larger ones). Say $\mathcal{M}$ is defined on $[-n,n]$. Now $M_{n+1} \in \mathcal{M}$ and $M_{-n-1} \in \mathcal{M}$ but $M_{n+1} \cap M_{-n-1} \cap [-n,n] = \emptyset$, a contradiction.

V.2.3

In lemma III.4.3 it was shown that if the T_1-space X admits an open and closed, continuous map onto $[0,1]$ then X must be pseudocompact. In the corresponding theorem III.4.3 it was claimed that the cone C(Y) of Y admits such a map if Y is countably compact. Of course countable compactness implies pseudocompactness and the two properties are equivalent for normal spaces.

The Tychonoff-plank $Y = w(\Omega) \times w(\omega)\backslash\{(\Omega,\omega)\}$ is an example of a pseudocompact, not countably compact space, for which the projection map $\pi: C(Y) \to [0,1]$ is not closed (here $w(\Omega)$, $w(\omega)$ are the sets of all ordinals

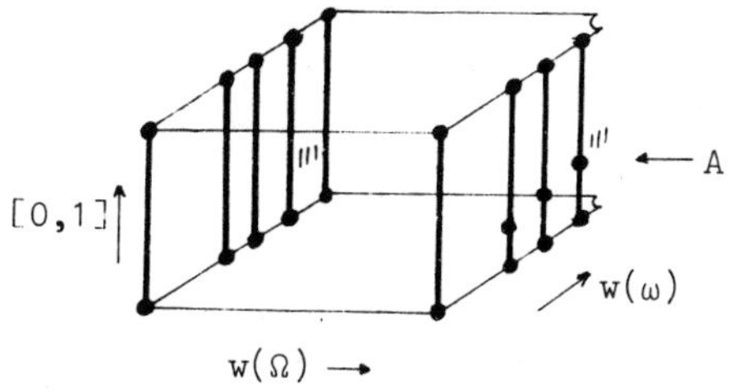

less than or equal to the first uncountable, resp. the first infinite ordinal). Indeed

$$A = \{(1/2-1/2n,\Omega,n)\in[0,1]\times Y/\{0\}\times Y =_{def} C(Y) \mid n\in\mathbb{N}\}$$

is a closed subset of C(Y), which does not have a closed projection on $[0,1]$, viz. $\{1/2-1/2n \mid n\in\mathbb{N}\}$.

Next we will construct an example of a pseudocompact, but not countably compact space X, that admits an open and closed, continuous map onto $[0,1]$.

Let Y be any infinite regular space for which all real-valued maps are constant. Let $A \subset Y$ be an infinite, discrete subset. Put $X = C(Y)\backslash(\{1\}\times(Y\backslash A))$. Then it is easily seen that the 'projection' $\pi: X \to [0,1]$ satisfies the requirements, while $\{1\} \times A$ is a closed, discrete, infinite subset of X.

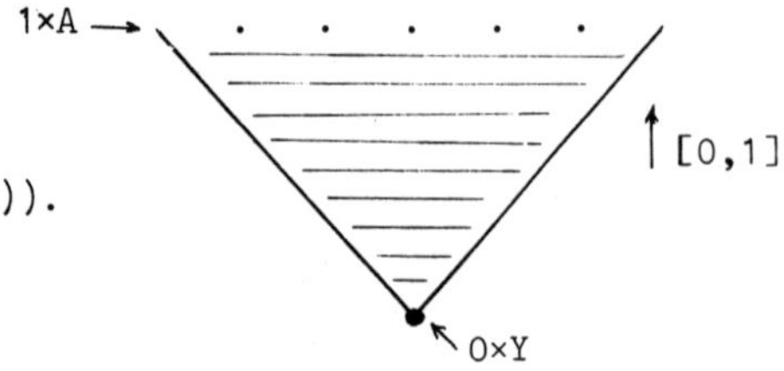

Finally we observe that the plane Peanocontinuum sketched here,

$\{(x,0) \mid -1\le x\le 1\} \cup \bigcup_{n=0}^{\infty} \{(\pm 2^{-n},y) \mid 0\le y\le 2^{-n}\}$,

admits no ϕ as required in the lemma III.4.3. Yet its superextension is contractible by II.4.7.

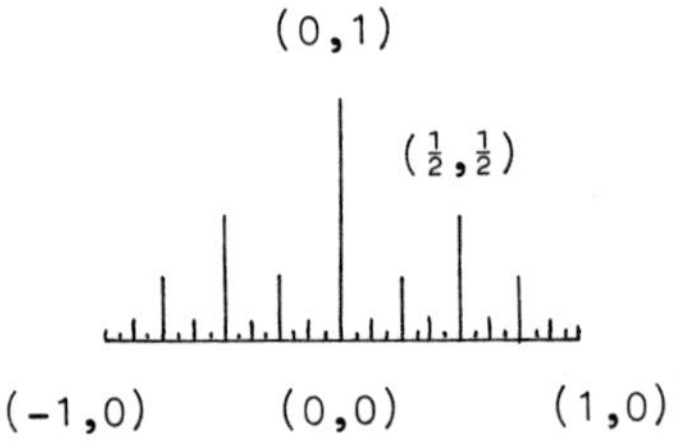

V.2.4

Let (M,d) be a complete metric space. Then $(\lambda_{comp}M,\bar{d})$ is a metric subspace of λM (cf. IV.3.8). Of course if M is compact, or discrete then $\lambda_{comp}M$ is also compact, or discrete respectively. In other cases however, $\bar{d}$ is not complete. We will illustrate this for $(M,d) = (\mathbb{R},d)$ with $d(a,b) = |a-b|$.

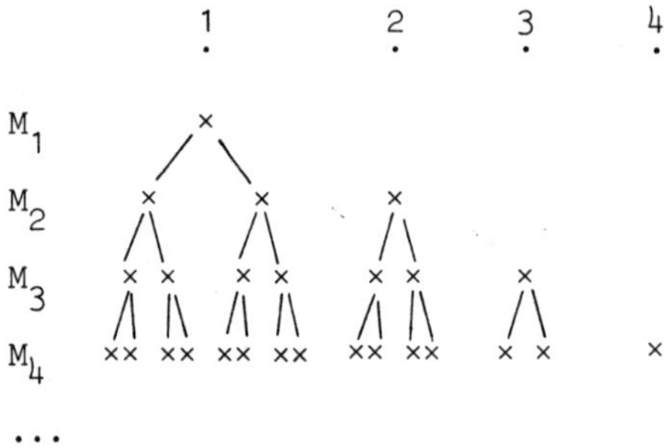

We define inductively the (2^n-1)-point-sets M_n in $\mathbb{R}$ as follows: $M_1 = \{1\}$. If M_n is defined, then define $M_{n+1} = \{n+1\} \cup \{p\pm q^{-n} \mid p\in M_n\}$. Observe that if $p,p' \in M_n$, then $|p-p'| > 4^{-n}$, so that M_{n-1} contains 2^n-1 points for $n \in \mathbb{N}$. Moreover for each k-point-set $S \subset M_n$:

(*) $\bar{U}_{4^{-n}}(K) \cap M_{n+1}$ contains $2k$ points.

Now define $\mathcal{M}_n \in \lambda_f\mathbb{R}$ on M_n by $\mathcal{M}_n = \{S\subset M_n \mid S$ contains at least 2^n points$\}$. Then it is easily seen that, because of (*), $\bar{d}(\mathcal{M}_n,\mathcal{M}_{n-1}) = 4^{-n}$, so that $(M_n)_n$ is a $\bar{d}$-Cauchy-sequence. Now assume it has a limit, say $M \in \lambda_{comp}R$. Then, for some $m \in \mathbb{N}$, M is defined on $[-m,m]$. Choose the points p,q such that $0 < p < q < m$ and

$$[p,q] \cap M_n = \emptyset \qquad \text{for all } n$$

and

$$\text{card}[0,p] \cap M_{m+1} = \text{card}[q,m+1/2] \cap M_{m+1}$$

We may even (and in fact we will) choose p and q such that

$$\forall m' > m \quad \text{card}[0,p] \cap M_{m'} = \text{card}[q,m+1/2] \cap M_{m'}$$

and

$$([0,p] \cup [m+1/2,\infty)) \cap M_{m'} \in M_{m'}$$

and

$$[q,\infty) \cap M_{m'} \qquad \in M_{m'}.$$

From this we may deduce that $\bar{d}(M_{m'},M) > (q-p)/2$ and hence $M_n \not\to M$, a contradiction. For if $\bar{d}(M_{m'},M) = a$, then $\bar{U}_a(S) \cap [-m,m] \in M$ for all $S \in M_{m'}$. In particular

$$\bar{U}_a(([0,p] \cup [m+1/2,\infty)) \cap M_{m'} \cap [-m,m]) \in M$$

and

$$\bar{U}_a(([q,\infty) \cap M_{m'} \cap [-m,m]) \in M.$$

Hence

$$\bar{U}_a[0,p] \cap \bar{U}_a[q,\infty) \neq \emptyset, \text{ i.e. } 2a > p-q.$$

V.3. OPEN QUESTIONS

The following questions, listed in a rather arbitrary order, are still open.

V.3.1. IS THE SUPEREXTENSION OF THE CLOSED UNIT INTERVAL HOMEOMORPHIC TO THE HILBERT-CUBE?

Recent developments in the theory of infinite dimensional spaces, such as the proof that the hyperspace of [0,1] is the Hilbertcube, Q, suggest that the answer may very well be both affirmative and hard to obtain. Most surprisingly seems maybe the suggested homogeneity, for which also in the case of the hyperspace however, there is no direct proof or indication. The widest classe of spaces X for which the obtained results do not disprove that λX is the Hilbertcube, and for which we hence may conjecture that $\lambda X \cong Q$, is the class of all metrizable continua. It may be useful to study first the following two questions.

V.3.2. IS THE SUPEREXTENSION OF THE CLOSED UNIT INTERVAL, OR OF ANY (METRIZABLE) CONTINUUM AN ABSOLUTE RETRACT?

Because of II.4.5 CORO 4 the question 'Is λM an AR for each metric AR M?' is equivalent to 'Is λQ an AR?', where Q is the Hilbertcube. Similarly the question 'Is λX an AR for each compact Hausdorff AR X?' reduces to 'Is λH an AR, for each product H of intervals [0,1]?'. Related to these questions is the following:

V.3.3. IS THE SUPEREXTENSION OF ANY (HAUSDORFF / METRIZABLE / COMPACT?) CONNECTED SPACE CONTRACTIBLE?

As to this question it may be remarked that the proof of the contractibility of λX for certain X given in III.4.3 seems rather ad hoc. It may well be possible to give a more "canonical" contraction. Cf. the contractibility of hyperspaces (see IV.1.7).

V.3.4

In [15] O'Connor proved that every compact metric space M has a (countable) closed subbase $\mathcal{S}$ that is both binary (i.e. each linked system in $\mathcal{S}$ has a non-empty intersection) and minimal (i.e. $\forall S \in \mathcal{S}$ $\mathcal{S} \setminus \{S\}$ is not a subbase for M anymore). This shows that every compact metrizable space is supercompact. In II.2.2.8 a compact T_1-space was demonstrated, that was not supercompact. But it is unknown whether e.g. βN or $\beta N \setminus N$ are supercompact:

Are there compact Hausdorff spaces, that are not supercompact?

It is not clear what the role is of the minimality of O'Connor's binary subbase. An earlier result of Van Emde Boas shows that all metric spaces have such a minimal subbase, [4].

V.3.5

In II.3.2 and III.3.3 it was shown that (weak) normality of S suffices to make $\lambda_S X$ (resp. $\beta_S X$) Hausdorff. In V.2.1 a weakly normal S_4 is defined for which $\lambda_{S_4}[0,1]$ is not Hausdorff, but also three other weakly normal (but not normal) subbases T are defined for which $\lambda_T[0,1]$ is Hausdorff. The question is still open to give necessary and sufficient, or at least weaker necessary conditions for S in order that $\lambda_S X$ (or $\beta_S X$) is Hausdorff. Two possible generalizations are known, that however do not seem very promising:

$\lambda_S X$ is Hausdorff (resp. $\beta_S X$ is) iff for each pair of (prime) mls's M, N there exist disjoint $S \in M$, $T \in N$ and there exist two (a finite number) $G_i \in M$ such that no G_i meets both S and T, and $\cup G_i = X$.

(cf. [9] p.7, G.A. Jensen). $\lambda_S X$ is Hausdorff if for each pair of disjoint sets $S,T \in S$ there exist finitely many $S_1,\ldots,S_n \in S$ such that

(i) S_i does not meet both S and T $\quad (i=1,\ldots,n)$

(ii) If $T_1,\ldots,T_n \in S$ and $T_i \cap S_i = \emptyset$ for $i=1,\ldots,n$, then $\{T_1,\ldots,T_n\}$ is not linked.

The latter condition is equivalent to $S_1^+ \cup \ldots S_n^+ = \lambda_S X$.

V.3.6

Fmls's were in this treatise only defined in subbases that contain all finite sets. This limited somewhat the obtained results. E.g. if S is a normal T_1-subbase of a (completely regular) connected space X, then λX was shown to be connected and locally connected (cf. III.4.1) by showing that the dense subspace $\lambda_f X$ has these properties. However in general no subspace corresponding to $\lambda_f X$ has been defined in $\lambda_S X$. We only know that $\lambda_S X$ has the same properties as λX, because Jensen's mapping theorem (II.4.5) shows that $\lambda_S X$ is a quotient of λX. If S does not contain all finite subsets of X, then we might now define fmls's in S as those mls's that are the images of fmls's in λX under Jensen's canonical quotient map. This means:

If S is a normal T_1-subbase, then an mls M in S is called an *fmls* in S if, for some finite subset $F \subset X$, $\{S \cap F \mid S \in M\}$ is linked.

It is the authors opinion that for a further development of the theory of superextensions a more general concept of fmls, maybe similar to the definition above, will be of importance. It may prove e.g. that $\lambda_S X$ is connected and locally connected for a much wider class of subbases than only the normal T_1-subbases and the subbases containing all finite sets. Recall however that not all subbases can be in this class: $\lambda_S[0,1]$ may be homeomorphic to [0,1] union one isolated point (V.2.1).

V.3.7

Examples V.2.1 suggest a.o. the following question:

Does there exist for every metrizable compactum M *a* T_1*-subbase S for* [0,1] *such that* $\lambda_S[0,1]\setminus i[0,1] \cong M$?

V.3.8

The subspace $\lambda_{comp}M$ of λM for a metric space M, has been described only very roughly yet. It is unknown whether e.g. $\lambda_{comp}\mathbb{R}$ is topologically complete (cf. V.2.4, V.2.2.c and IV.3.8). A problem that often recurs is: If $\{X_\alpha \mid \alpha\}$ is a linked family of closed sets, then $\{X_\alpha^+ \cap \lambda_{comp}X \mid \alpha\}$ is centered, because there even is an fmls in each finite intersection (III.3.1). However $\cap\{X_\alpha^+ \cap \lambda_{comp}X \mid \alpha\}$ is non-empty (if and) only if there is a closed, compact set C in X such that for all pairs α,α' $X_\alpha \cap X_{\alpha'} \cap C \neq \emptyset$. The problem then is to find such a C, or to give sufficient conditions for its existence. Observe that, even if X_α is compact, X_α^+ is not, unless X_α is a singleton or X is compact.

Also unknown are sufficient conditions (weaker than compactness or discreteness) under which $\lambda_{comp}X$ is a Baire-space (i.e. no open set is meager).

Finally, it still can be conjectured (cf. V.1.2) that

$$\lambda_{comp}\mathbb{R} \cong l_2,$$

the separable Hilbert-space. This would be interesting especially if one could prove that $\lambda[0,1] \cong$ Hilbert-cube, because $\lambda_{comp}\mathbb{R} \cong \lambda_{comp}(0,1)$, which is a dense subspace of $\lambda[0,1]$ (III.3.3 + IV.3.10).

V.3.9. (due to Dr. A.B. Paalman-de Miranda)

Theorem II.5.17 (" $\lambda_S X = \lambda_{S'}\beta_S X$ ") suggests the following question:

Can every (T_2?) *compactification of any* ($T_{3\frac{1}{2}}$) *space* X *be obtained as* $\beta_S X$ *by a suitable choice of the subbase S?*

An affirmative answer would imply that the theory could be concentrated on superextensions of compact spaces only. But in addition it may shed new light upon the longstanding analoguous question for Wallman-type-compactifications. This problem (viz. can every T_2-compactification of any $T_{3\frac{1}{2}}$-space X be obtained as $\omega_S X$) is at the moment only solved for some special cases (e.g. metrizable compactifications).

REFERENCES

[1] J.M. AARTS, J. de GROOT, R.H. McDOWELL — *Cotopology for metrizable spaces.* Duke Math. J. 37 (1970), 291-295. MR 41 #4488.

[2] A.E. BROUWER, A. VERBEEK — *Counting families of mutually intersection sets.* (to appear)

[3] A. CSÁSZAR — *Wallman-type compactifications.* Periodica Mathematica Hungarica 1 (1971), 55-80.

[4] P. van EMDE BOAS — *Minimally generated topologies.* Proc. Internat. Sympos. on Topology and its Applications (Herceg-Novi, 1968), pp.146-152. Savez Društava Mat. Fiz. i Astronom Belgrade, 1969. MR 42 #6773.

[5] J. de GROOT — *Non-Archimedian metrics in topology.* Proc. Amer. Math. Soc. 7 (1956), 948-953. MR 18 #325.

[6] J. de GROOT — *Supercompactness and superextensions.* Contributions to extension theory of topological structures. Symp. Berlin 1967. Deutsche Verlag der Wissenschaften, Berlin 1969, p. 89-90. MR 39 #6268.

[7] J. de GROOT, J.M. AARTS — *Complete regularity as a separation axiom.* Can. J. Math. 21 (1969), 96-105. MR 38 #5160.

[8] J. de GROOT, G.A. JENSEN, A. VERBEEK — *Superextensions.* Proc. Internat. Sympos. on Topology and its Applications (Herceg-Novi, 1968), pp.176-178. Savez Društava Mat. Fiz. i Astronom., Belgrade, Belgrade, 1969.

[9] J. de GROOT, G.A. JENSEN, A. VERBEEK — *Superextensions.* Research report ZW 1968-07, Mathematisch Centrum, Amsterdam, 1968. MR 40 #6508.

[10] P. HAMBURGER — *A general method to give internal characterizations of completely regular and Tychonoff spaces.* (to appear)

[11] I. JUHASZ — *Cardinal functions in Topology.* Mathematical Centre Tracts, 34, Mathematisch Centrum, Amsterdam, 1971.

[12] D. KLEITMAN — *On Dedekind's problem: The number of monotone boolean functions.* Proc. Amer. Math. Soc. 21 (1969) 677-682. MR 39 #2674.

[13] I.K. LIFANOV — *Dimensionality of products of bicompact spaces.* Soviet Math. Dokl. 9 (1968), 1280-1283. Dokl. Akad. Nauk SSR 182 (1968), 1274-1277. MR 38 #6556.

[14] E.A. MICHAEL — *Topologies on spaces of subsets.* Trans. Amer. Math. Soc. 71 (1951), 152-182. MR 13 #54.

[15] J.L. O'CONNER — *Supercompactness of compact metric spaces.* Indag. Math. ≡ Nederl. Akad. Wetensch. Proc. Ser. A. 73 (1970), 30-34. MR 41 #9202.

[16] L.J.W. SMITH — *On the extension of completely regular spaces.* Thesis Univ. of Florida, 1967.

[17] H. WALLMAN — *Lattices and topological spaces.* Ann. Math. 39 (1938), 112-126.

LIST OF SYMBOLS

Special assumptions

From page 45 on it is assumed that

- X is a T_1-space
- $\mathcal{S}$ is a closed T_1-subbase for X
- $\mathcal{G}$ is the family of non-empty closed subsets of X
- $\mathcal{O}$ is the family of proper open subsets of X
- $\mathcal{Z}$ is the family of non-empty zerosets of X
- $i: X \to \lambda_{\mathcal{S}}X$ is the canonical embedding.

In I.2, III.2, III.3, and III.4 we assume that

$$P_f X \subset \mathcal{S} \subset PX.$$

In IV.2 and IV.3 it is understood that

$$X = (M,d)$$

is a metric space, which is compact in IV.2 and non-compact in IV.3.

Special symbols, such as $\mathbb{R}$, PX, $d(X)$, $\lambda_{\mathcal{S}}X$, π_i are listed in the index.

Operators

$A^{\cap}$, $A^{\cup}$, $A^{f\cap}$, $A^{f\cup}$	(for a family A)	45
A^{+}, S^{+}	(for $A \subset X$, $S \in \mathcal{S}$)	45
A_{MIN}	(for a family A)	6, 13, 39
$\bar{f}$	(for a function $f: X \to Y$)	19, 55, 89ff
$\bar{d}$	(for a metric d)	114
$\underline{M}$	(for a pre-mls M)	5, 11
$(M,x_1,\ldots,x_n) = f_M((x_1,\ldots,x_n)) = \bar{f}(M)$		86
$\bar{U}_{\varepsilon}$	(= closed ε-neighbourhood)	113
A^{-}	(for a subset A of a topological space) = = the closure of A	

Variables and constants

The symbols	are mostly used for
$A, B, \ldots$	arbitrary sets

X,Y,...	T_1-spaces
F,G,H,S,T,...	(closed) subsets X,Y,...
O,U,V,...	(open) subsets of X,Y,...
p,q,r,x,y,z,...	arbitrary elements or points
j,k,l,m,n,...	natural numbers (recall that i: $X \to \lambda_S X$)
d	a metric or the density d(X)
d_H	the Hausdorff metric of HX
f,g,h,ϕ,ψ,...	(continuous) maps
H	homotopy (sometimes)
$\mathcal{A}$,$\mathcal{B}$,...	arbitrary families
$\mathcal{M}$,$\mathcal{N}$,$\mathcal{P}$,$\mathcal{K}$,$\mathcal{H}$,	linked families, pre-mls's or mls's
C	the compact, closed subsets of X

INDEX

I'll never forget the day my first
book is published
Every chapter I stole from
somewhere else
Index I copied from old Vladivostok
telephon directory
This book was sensational

(Lobachevsky - by Tom Lehrer)

(the numbers behind the words refer to pages, or, if in square brackets, to references; the first number usually refers to the definition, other numbers refer to the most important occurrences; the index does not only contain references to the newly defined notions and notations but also to many theorems via their keynotions)

ERRATA

	for ...	please read:
i_4	system	systems
ii^2	consider	considers
ii^7	. the	. The
iii^9	stronly	strongly
3^2	$S = A \cup B \cup$	$PS = A \cup B \cup$
3_{11}	further on	in the sequel
4^{13}	$x \notin G$	$p \notin G$
4^{15}	contain x	contain p
7^6	$\phi^{-1} \geq \pi$	$\phi^{-1}I \geq \pi$
9^2	$-n,\dots,0,-2$	$-n,\dots,-2$
9^{11}	$\dots,k\}\setminus M_k$	$\dots,\lvert k\rvert\}\setminus M_k$
10^{13}	$0 \in S$	$0 \notin S$
11^{12}	$\{S' \in \mathcal{S}' \mid$	$\{S' \in \mathcal{S} \mid$
11_1	$P \cup \{S\}$	$\mathcal{P} \cup \{S\}$
12^7	of $\mathcal{S}$ contains	of S contains
13_6	But	By
in 15_4 and figure at 16		$a = a_0$
16^9	OR	OF
16_2	part	past
17^9	(v)	(vi)
17^{16}	by (a) and 1.2	by (i) and I.1.4.c
18_1	$\subset \mathcal{S} \subset$	$\subset \mathcal{S}_\alpha \subset$
27_2	$\exists S' \in M$	$\exists S' \subset M$
28_8	such	each
31^1	$\mathcal{M}$ contains	$\mathcal{M}$ is free and contains
33^5	1,2,3,4,5	{1,2,3,4,5}
33_5	an	and
39_{12}	I.2.8.(c)	I.1.8.(c)
49_7	place	plane
49_3	homeomorfic	homeomorphic
50^3	So far one	So for one
50_{10}	s has for neighbourhoods only all	the neigh-bourhoods of s are

	for ...	please read:
52	figure	interchange A'_1 and A'_2
57^{11}	$i = 1,2$	$i = 0,1$
59^3	subbases	subbasis
61_5	$H_t : H \mid$	$H_t = H \mid$
68_1	lead	led
69^{14}	necessary	necessarily
70_7	$\lambda_S(x) \to \lambda_T(x)$	$\lambda_S(X) \to \lambda_T(X)$
$71_{12,13}$	$\forall T \in \mathcal{T}$	$\forall T \in \mathcal{T}\setminus\mathcal{S}$
72^9	see 3.3(iii) and cf. 4.2	see II.3.4.iii and cf. II.4.2
77_1	problem it is	problem is, that it is

79

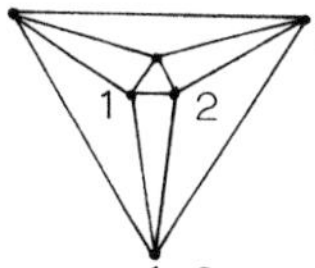

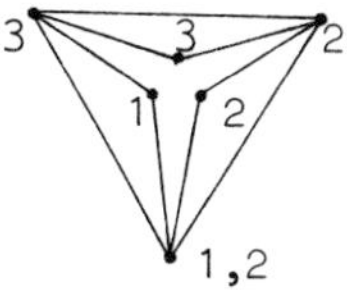

	for ...	please read:
82^1	proceded	continued
88^{10}	for $i\in$	for some $i\in$
92^7	$\forall P \in \lambda_f(S)$	$\forall \mathcal{P} \in \lambda_f(S)$
92_{11}	belongs	belongs to
98^1	Susling	Suslin
99^1	II.7.5.b	III.2.5.b
109^{10}	$\dots,\lambda(k)\}\mid$	$\dots,k\}\mid$
109^{11}	throught	thought
117^7	inclusion	inclusions
117_{10}	$(U_\varepsilon(s_i))^+$	$(U_\varepsilon(S_i))^+$
118^{10}	*(if* λX	*(iff* X
128_7	defining	definition
129^{24}	as	like
135^2	In particular	So for these X
135_2	our	out
137^9	homeomorph	homeomorphic
$55_6, 129^{4,6}$	Cech	Čech
$54^8, 75_{11}, 85^8, 87_{6,9}, 102^{17}, 142_5$	R, Z or N	$\mathbb{R}$, $\mathbb{Z}$ or $\mathbb{N}$